Crime Writing

Studymates

Algebra and Graphs
Better English (2nd Ed)
Better French (3rd Ed)
Better French 2
Better German
Better Spanish
British History 1870-1918
Business Communication
Business Coaching
Calculus
Chemistry: AS Chemistry Explained
Chemistry: Chemistry Calculations Explained (3rd Ed)
Crime Writing: How to Write the Science
European History
Genetics
Ghost Writing
Growing Workplace Champions
Hitler and Nazi Germany (3rd Ed)
Lenin, Stalin and Communist Russia (2nd Ed)
Marketing Principles for Business
Numeracy for Health Professionals
Numeracy for Health Professionals: Scientific Application
Organic Chemistry
Perfect Grammar
Plant Physiology
Practical Drama (2nd Ed)
Professional Writing
Project Management (2nd Ed)
Shakespeare
Social Anthropology (2nd Ed)
Starting to Write

Starting Statistics

Statistics for Social Sciences

Study Skills

Studying Poetry (2ndEd)

The Academic Essay (3rdEd)

The English Reformation

The Theatre Makers (2ndEd)

Trigonometry

Understanding Algebra (2ndEd)

Understanding Literature and Film (2ndEd)

Understanding Maths (5thEd)

Understanding the Numbers

Warfare1792-1918

Workforce Wellbeing

Writing Crime Fiction

Writing for Children

Writing How to Articles and Books

Writing and Imagery

Writing Science Fiction

Writing Soap

Writing TV Scripts

Your Master's Thesis (2ndEd)

Your Ph.D. Thesis

Many other titles in preparation

To Walt Patterson, who published my first magazine piece and encouraged me to write over many years, and to all those crime writers who strive for scientific accuracy.

Disclaimer

The information given in this book is given as guidance for the creation of crime stories for enlightenment/ entertainment and the critical review of said stories. Neither the author nor the publisher (nor any/all of the publisher's agents) can be held responsible for any actions/outcomes, legal or otherwise, that may result from the publication of this information.

Crime Writing

How to Write the Science

Brian Price

I would like to record my thanks first of all to my wife, Jen, whose idea this book was and whose eagle-eyed checking and constructive comments have improved it enormously.

I would also like to thank Dr Don Emerson and Dr Andy Tubb, Senior Lecturer in Forensic Science at the University of the West of England, for their comments on the first draft and Dr Richard Lawson for helping me with medical aspects.

 978 1-84285-537- 9

Reprinted 2019

First published by Studymates, Abergele

Website: www.graham-lawler.com

Book Cover and Typesetting by **SHED MEDIA**

Printed in Europe

Contents

Introduction

6 Firearms 127

7 Weapons and Tactics 153

Part 1: Means of murder

Introduction

What this book is - and isn't

The aim of this book is to help crime writers to avoid mistakes - not with grammar, spelling or plotting but with those aspects of science which inevitably impinge on their writing. Poisons, firearms, explosions, fires and the effects of weapons are all governed by the laws of science and it is all too easy to use received wisdom to break these laws. Increasingly, writers seek to get the science right by carrying out detailed research and consulting experts. This book should suffice in many cases and provide signposts to further sources of information in others. Of course, experienced crime writers will be aware of much of the material in this book but I hope there will be something in it for everyone, not just those new to crime fiction. Who knows - there may be some ideas for novel plots! Although aimed at writers, it will also interest readers of crime fiction and students embarking upon creative writing, forensic science, and criminology courses.

The book is not a murderer's manual. I do not include detailed descriptions of how to make bombs, prepare poisons or set fires. All the information included is available from open sources without recourse to the dark web or *The Anarchist's Cookbook*. It would be unethical, dangerous and possibly illegal to include too much detail and I hope that writers using the book, and other sources, will exercise similar restraint. Neither I nor the publisher can be held responsible if someone misuses information which is already in the public domain.

I do not include details of autopsies, the mechanics of crime scene investigations or many details of the techniques used in forensic science laboratories – there are plenty of other sources for this type of information. The chapters on DNA and Forensics are intended to provide a flavour of selected topics, introduce some recent developments and clarify a number of misconceptions.

The book is written primarily from a U.K. standpoint in the early part of the 21st century. Laws, particularly those relating to firearms and the availability of chemicals, vary widely from country to country and have also evolved over time. Authors setting their work in non-U.K. locations, or earlier times, should investigate relevant controls.

No prior knowledge of science is assumed and some technical terms are explained in the Glossary.

References and suggestions for further reading appear at the end of the book on a chapter-by-chapter basis. Many are internet-based and vary from newspaper reports to academic papers, all of which can be found without access to an academic library. A few references are to out-of-print books but these can usually be obtained via online book dealers. Some sources may not be sufficient for an academic thesis but I am satisfied that those cited are sufficiently reliable for the context in which they are used.

In the book I refer to many fiction works where the author has used the principles or items I describe, completely - or at least reasonably - correctly. I also point out mistakes in novels and visual media without naming and shaming the authors.

Inevitably, mistakes may have crept into my own writing and I welcome comments, corrections and updates via my website.

Brian Price

www.crimewriterscience.co.uk.

CHAPTER 1: POISONS: GENERAL PRINCIPLES

Poisons have been a popular means of disposing of people in literature, from Chaucer onwards. Requiring only ruthlessness rather than physical strength or proficiency with weapons, poisoning has often been considered a woman's means of murder but there have been plenty of notorious male poisoners in real life. In this Chapter I will set out some basic principles of toxicology - what poisons are and how they affect us - and will also show how difficult it is to get hold of them.

What is a poison?

The answer to this question, in short, is almost anything. It's all a question of dose. Too much oxygen or too much water - both essential to life - can be dangerous in the wrong place. Similarly, a very small quantity of cyanide or arsenic is harmless. This principle was set out by the 16th century physician Paracelsus who wrote "Poison is in everything and no thing is without poison. The dosage makes it either a poison or a remedy." For the purposes of crime writing, however, we are normally looking at chemicals which can kill or seriously harm people in doses of up to a few grams.

Getting it into the body

Apart from corrosive chemicals, such as strong acids and alkalies, poisons only work once they are in the body. In most cases, in fiction and in real life, the victim swallows the poison, usually in food or drink. It then has to get to the parts of the body on which it acts, which takes time. Depending on the chemical involved, some may be absorbed through the linings of the mouth and throat (mucous membranes). Generally, poisons are not readily absorbed through the stomach wall (alcohol is an exception) but when they reach the intestines absorption is much more extensive.[1] Once absorbed, the chemical is transported to the parts of the body on which it acts but the first organ encountered by swallowed poisons is the liver.

Most poisons take 15-20 minutes to take effect once swallowed although absorption through mucous membranes is quicker - which is why people snort cocaine and crack rather than swallowing them. If the victim has eaten recently it can take longer since food rich in fat and protein delays absorption. Fizzy drinks can speed up absorption, however, since they cause the stomach to empty more quickly[2]. The physical form of the poison also affects absorption - tablets take time to dissolve in gastric juices while liquids or substances in solution are ready to be absorbed. The poison may be altered by the digestive system and the liver before it reaches the target - in some cases this alteration converts the poison to a more dangerous form and in others it may partially destroy it.

Inhalation is a quick way of getting a substance into the bloodstream which is why people smoke tobacco and cannabis rather than swallowing them (although some cannabis users eat it in cakes for a more gradual effect). Gases are the obvious examples but liquids, in the form of mists, and even dusts can enter the body in this way. Christopher Fowler used this device in *Bryant and May off the Rails* (2010) where a victim was sprayed with a nicotine solution which would have been inhaled as well as absorbed through the skin.

The skin is a pretty good barrier against noxious material entering the body but it is not perfect. Some substances can penetrate this barrier - organic chemicals rather than inorganic ones in the main - and can be conveyed quickly to vital systems by the bloodstream. Nicotine and hormone replacement therapy patches are examples of non-lethal skin penetration, but Novichok in Wiltshire (see p58) was much more dangerous. Aconitine (see below) can be absorbed through bare skin in doses sufficient to cause numbness simply by brushing against the Monkshood plant and gardeners unwise enough to grow it should wear gloves when handling the plant.

The quickest way of getting a poison through the skin is to inject it. Injecting a substance into a vein is the most effective way of enabling it to work (injecting into an artery is not feasible) but this is not particularly easy, requiring, as it does, some skill and a compliant victim. An injection into a muscle is easier but can take time and is often painful for the recipient. Once in the muscle, the chemical must diffuse into blood vessels to be carried to its target and this delays its effect - midazolam, for instance, takes three to five minutes to produce full sedation when injected intravenously but 15 minutes when injected into a muscle.[3]

Do remember that injections leave traces. Intravenous injections can leave a spot of blood at the surface and lead to slight bruising under the skin where bleeding has occurred - as anyone who has given a blood sample will testify - and puncture marks are detectable at most injection sites. Someone very skilled at giving injections may be able to minimise the evidence - provided that the victim does not resist - but a careful examination at autopsy will normally find it. Traces of the injected material may remain around the injection point, especially if the injection is into a muscle, and tissue will be removed around any such sites at autopsy for analysis. If the death is not regarded as suspicious, and a post mortem is not performed, a small needle mark may be missed but injecting a significant volume of liquid into a muscle or just under the skin could leave damage which even a cursory examination would spot. It has been suggested that an injection between the toes or under the tongue might not be detected. This would depend on luck and the skill of the pathologist.

Medically, some injections are given subcutaneously - just under the skin - but only small volumes of material are possible. Poison darts, as used by hunters in South America, will rarely penetrate a vein and it takes a while for the subcutaneous poison to take effect. For highly toxic substances - the toxin produced by poison dart frogs, for instance - this route may be fatal. Kathy Reichs used a poisoned dart coated with abrin in *Flash and Bones* (2011) although the target recovered as only a small dose was injected.

In 2015 a Chinese police officer was reported to have been killed by a syringe-like dart, fired from a crossbow, containing succinylcholine[4a] and in 2016, Chinese scientists reported three cases of homicide using darts coated in succinylcholine fired from a special dart gun[5].

In some cases a substance may produce effects only if injected. Propofol, for instance, is a powerful anaesthetic when given intravenously but it does not produce sedation or anaesthesia when taken orally since what little of the drug is absorbed from the gut is rapidly broken down in the liver[6].

Getting it out of the body

Once a poison is in the body several things can happen to it. It may be eliminated via the kidneys, lungs or faeces (USA = feces). Vomiting can clear some materials out of the stomach before they are absorbed - antimony is a case in point - but not always in time. Some may be sweated out through the skin. Poisons may be stored in tissues. Lead, for instance, is trapped in bones and teeth while some pesticides, such as DDT, are stored in fat. Metals and many drugs are incorporated into hair as it grows, which provides a useful marker of exposure. Absorbed chemicals are changed by a whole raft of processes which convert them into different substances known as metabolites. It is the liver's job to detoxify harmful substances into chemicals which can be excreted ("detox diets" are a nonsense unless you are missing both liver and kidneys) so non-metallic poisons may be broken down and eliminated by this organ. Unfortunately, the liver is vulnerable to the effects of some poisons - large doses of paracetamol and the toxins in some fungi can destroy it. In many cases there is a race against time to get rid of a poison before it can cause fatal damage. With fast-acting poisons, e.g. cyanides, in sufficient quantity this race is usually lost.

Half-Life

The rate at which a poison is broken down or excreted from the body is determined by its half-life. This is the time taken for its concentration to fall to half its original level. So, if you start with 100mg per litre of something in the blood with a half-life of one hour, an hour later there will be 50mg/l. Another hour later there will be 25mg/l, an hour after that there will be 12.5mg/l and so on. (In mathematical terms, the rate of removal is proportional to the amount present).

Chemicals with a short half-life tend to disappear rapidly from the tissues which makes them difficult to detect date rape drugs are an important example (see Chapter 3). Their actions also tend to decline rapidly although there may be residual effects for some time. Not all poisons follow this pattern: alcohol is eliminated from the body at a steady rate regardless of the concentration.

Acute versus chronic

Acute poisoning means fatal, or non-fatal but serious, effects from a single dose of a poison. Symptoms usually develop quickly and rapid treatment is needed to deal with them. If the patient survives there may be some long-term damage to vulnerable systems but the principal effects are over. In fiction, Agatha Christie's *Sparkling Cyanide* (1945) describes a case of acute poisoning: the Novichok poisonings in Wiltshire provide real life examples (see p58).

Chronic poisoning occurs when smaller doses of a poison are administered over prolonged periods so that the substance either builds up in the body or its effects gradually debilitate the victim, sometimes leading to death. Chronic poisoning by thallium was used by Christie in *The Pale Horse* (1961) while, in real life, the same metal was used by Graham Young to poison his workmates.

Case study: Thallium at home and work[7]

Although he started his poisoning career with antimony, Graham Young is best known as Britain's thallium poisoner. In 1962 he killed his stepmother with a lethal dose of thallium while simultaneously poisoning, chronically but non-fatally, his sister, his father and a school friend. Although not charged with killing his stepmother, he was convicted of poisoning the others and sent to Broadmoor, the psychiatric secure hospital. Eight years later he was discharged and got a job at a photographic equipment company where he proceeded to slowly poison eight of his workmates, two of them fatally, with antimony and thallium. This time he was convicted of murder and sent down for life. He died in prison in 1990.

Tolerance

Absorbing small, non-fatal, doses of some poisons can lead to tolerance developing. The body adapts and, ultimately, can handle doses which would be harmful - even fatal - to unexposed people. Compare the results of a teetotaller drinking half a bottle of whisky over half-an-hour with the effects of the same dosage on a seasoned alcoholic. The former could quite possibly die from acute alcohol poisoning: the latter would be drunk but alive. In 2018 a woman unused to alcohol died of respiratory failure after sharing a bottle and a half of wine with a friend[8]. Similarly, it would be more difficult to poison a heavy smoker with nicotine than someone who had never smoked - the smoker's body is used to handling nicotine and has built up defences to do so.

Some individuals can become immune to snake bites following repeated exposure[9] and tolerance to arsenic was used in Dorothy L. Sayers' *Strong Poison* (1930). In this novel the murderer had built up a tolerance to the poison and safely ate the same food as his victim who subsequently died. Tolerance only goes so far, however. Heroin addicts who can survive doses which would be highly dangerous to non-users are still killed on occasions when much purer versions of the drug replace their usual, highly diluted, supplies, or when they lose their tolerance after a period remaining clear of heroin.

A fatal dose

People react differently to poisons. Some people are particularly sensitive, responding badly to a dose which would have no effect on others. Conversely, others can tolerate doses which would prove lethal to many. The reasons for this vary - some people are more or less efficient at eliminating the poison; some are better at detoxifying it and in some individuals the systems attacked are just not as vulnerable. This means that you cannot predict the lethal dose for everyone in the population - although a very large dose of something highly poisonous is unlikely to leave anyone unscathed. Details of potentially lethal doses of some poisons appear in Chapter 2 under the respective headings but they range from a few nanograms (billionths of a gram) to several grams.

LD50

You may have heard the term "LD50". This is the amount of a substance which kills half the population of experimental animals when tested on them and is usually expressed as milligrams (or micrograms) of substance per kilogram of animal body weight. For obvious reasons there are no human experimental LD50 data available. You cannot extrapolate animal LD50s to humans simply by multiplying the dose to account for the larger human body weight. Laboratory animals may respond very differently from humans although it is fair to say that if only a few micrograms of something kills half the individuals in a population of animals it is likely to be highly poisonous to people.

One point worth remembering is that age can affect someone's response to a poison. Children, especially young ones, are generally more sensitive to many poisons while elderly people are also vulnerable. Health problems can also make people more at risk - someone with lung disease is likely to be harmed more by inhaling chlorine than someone young and healthy while a person with heart disease is likely to die from smaller doses of substances which affect the heart than someone free of cardiac problems.

How do they work?

Disregarding corrosive poisons such as sulfuric* acid, which wreck any tissues with which they come into contact, most poisons act by affecting vital processes which go on within our cells. Frequently, this involves preventing enzymes from working. Enzymes are the cell's catalysts - they regulate what happens and how fast. If they are disrupted, processes can slow down, accelerate out of control or simply stop. Nerve agents such as Novichok, (see Chapter 2), work by inhibiting an enzyme which regulates how nerves transmit messages. Arsenic, in its more lethal form (see Chapter 2), inhibits a whole range of enzymes which is why the symptoms of arsenic poiso ing are often diverse.

* Here we are using the modern international spelling. In a UK novel "sulphuric" is acceptable, as is "sulphur" for sulfur.

Some poisons - ricin and some fungal toxins are examples - an affect how cells reproduce and repair by interfering with the process by which cells make proteins from the information encoded in DNA (see Chapter 9). These poisons take longer to work but can be lethal in small doses. Others, such as thallium, can substitute for chemicals in the body which are involved in key processes, thereby causing havoc within the tissues.

Working together

Chemicals can work together in affecting the body's systems. Alcohol will make many of the date rape drugs described in Chapter 3 more effective and, as a respiratory depressant, it can form a lethal combination with the barbiturate sleeping tablets widely prescribed in the 1950s and 1960s until safer alternatives became available. It also makes benzodiazepines such as diazepam (Valium) more potent.

An ingenious attempt to throw suspicion away from a murderer involved the poison tetrodotoxin, although not as the primary cause of death. In 1987 a Japanese woman was murdered by her husband with aconitine but tetrodotoxin was also found in her blood. It was thought that the tetrodotoxin was given to delay the effects of the aconite so the killer would not be suspected of poisoning her[10].

Antidotes

Not all interactions increase the harm done and for some poisons there are recognised antidotes and treatments to reverse their toxic effects or protect the body from damage. Atropine, a highly toxic chemical derived from Deadly Nightshade, is one of the drugs used to treat poisoning by nerve agents[11] and similar compounds. Physostigmine (formerly known as eserine), itself a highly toxic compound, can be used to treat atropine poisoning[12]. Opiate overdoses are treated with an injection of naloxone which can save the patient's life if given in time. Metal poisons such as lead can be removed from the body by one of a group of chemicals called chelating agents – these grab hold of the poison and keep it from doing harm until the combination can be excreted. Diethylene glycol poisoning is treated with alcohol which competes for the enzyme that converts diethylene glycol to more harmful metabolites, giving the body more time to excrete the initial poison[13].

In many cases there is no specific antidote so supportive treatment (keeping the patient hydrated, nourished and rested) is the only option. If the poison has been swallowed the first step is to wash out the stomach with a mixture of water and charcoal pumped in through a tube (this is called gastric lavage). Any poison remaining in the stomach is adsorbed by the charcoal and the mixture is withdrawn through the tube. Needless to say, this is an unpleasant procedure.

Sedation, fluids and oxygen may be provided to keep the patient alive while the poison works its way through the system, hopefully not causing too much damage before it leaves. In some cases, however, this may be too late. Once a fatal dose of the poisons in certain fungi (Death Cap, Destroying Angel) is absorbed death cannot be prevented except, perhaps, with a liver transplant. Similarly, a large dose of the herbicide paraquat will kill unless a lung transplant is available.

Delayed action

Some poisons take a considerable time to kill once a fatal dose has been ingested. Paracetamol overdoses, unless dealt with quickly as shown above, take several days as the liver is slowly destroyed and some fungal poisons behave in the same way, although there is an initial period of recovery. Paraquat poisoning has a similar delay and ricin, too, takes days to prove fatal.

Carcinogens

Carcinogens are substances which cause cancer, common examples being asbestos, tobacco smoke and benzene. They would not normally be considered as murder weapons since it can take many years for a cancer to develop following exposure to a carcinogen and the susceptibility of people varies greatly. If you swallow a large dose of an acute poison it is highly likely that you will die but if you swallow a dose of a carcinogen there is no guarantee you will develop cancer - although your chances of doing so will undoubtedly increase. In 2018, however, a graduate student at Queen's University in Kingston, Canada, admitting poisoning a fellow worker with the carcinogen N-nitrosodimethylamine (NDMA). The victim suspected someone was tampering with his food at work so he set up a camera which recorded the culprit adding the poison to his bread. NDMA has caused fatal poisoning but in this case the victim survived, although he did suffer vomiting after one attack[14]. The grimmest aspect of this case is that he will never know how likely he is to contract cancer as a result.

Biological agents

Strictly speaking, poisonous plants are biological agents which could be used to murder but in this section I will discuss micro-organisms and animals rather than their vegetable counterparts. Microbes and the chemicals they produce can be deadly - botulinum toxin, for instance, is produced by a species of bacterium under specific conditions (see Chapter 2).

Common infections are unlikely to be practical as murder weapons, although someone with flu sneezing over a person who has a badly weakened immune system could possibly bring about their death. Similarly, giving someone food poisoning from food known to be contaminated is likely to make them feel ill but would not normally kill unless they were already weak. Inducing septicaemia in a victim is also hit and miss, especially while antibiotics are still available to treat bacterial infections, but Agatha Christie did use this method in *Murder is Easy* (1939) - pus from an infected cat's ear was introduced into a victim's cut with fatal results.

Growing pathogenic organisms in the home, without contracting the disease, is not easy. Specialist equipment and training is required. It can be done, however, and the anthrax bacterium, *Bacillus anthracis*, can be cultivated with the benefit of only a year's university training in microbiology[15]. It is less easy to prepare anthrax in a weaponised form - the bacterium's spores are the infectious agent and obtaining these in sufficient quantity requires considerable skill. Anthrax was developed as a biological warfare agent (an episode of *Foyle's War*[a] featured an accident with this material) and has also been used in an instance of bioterrorism in the U.S. In 2001, envelopes containing anthrax spores were sent to news outlets and two senators via the U.S. mail. Five of the 22 people infected died[16].
In fiction, Agatha Christie used anthrax in *Cards on the Table*

(1930). Unlike bacteria, viruses cannot be cultivated without considerable skill and highly specialised facilities since they need living hosts to multiply.

Venomous invertebrates have been used to attack people in fiction from the *Scolopendra* centipede in Ian Fleming's *Dr No* (1958) (a harmless spider in the film) to Paul Finch's spiders and a scorpion in *Hunted* (2015). The lethality of invertebrate venoms is often over-rated, although death from Cone Shell venom featured, accurately, in Season 4 of *The Bridge*[b] - some 70% of people stung by the species *Conus geographus* die if they don't receive treatment[17].

Most spiders, including the notorious Black Widow, do not inflict fatal bites and deaths are very rare - even in Australia which hosts the Funnel Web and Redback species[18]. In the U.S. the only really dangerous spider is the Brown Recluse - again, deaths are very rare although the bite symptoms can be extremely unpleasant. The antivenom may be more dangerous than the spider bite [19]. Some vulnerable people may be at greater risk - children and people with specific allergies - but the pain caused from a bite could have other consequences such as a car crash if inflicted while the victim is driving.

Scorpions, too, are not always as venomous as they are portrayed. The large Emperor Scorpion, available in pet shops, may give a painful sting but is not dangerous. Some smaller species, such as the Fat Tail and Death Stalker scorpions can be lethal - troops posted to the Middle East are taught to look out for them. Amy Stewart's book *Wicked Bugs*[20] provides more details of these, and other, potentially harmful invertebrates.

Vertebrates, however, can be much more dangerous. One of the most powerful poisons known in nature is batrachotoxin, a complex of chemicals secreted by poison dart frogs. The frogs do not make it from their own resources but derive it from their diet of specific invertebrates. Without this diet the frogs are harmless and the specimens on sale through pet dealers contain no poison. It is unlikely that your villain would be able to collect these frogs in Central and South America, smuggle them into the U.K. and extract the toxin before it fades away, so they are not practical as murder weapons.

Snakes are a different matter. Our only native venomous snake, the Adder, is rarely dangerous except to children and those particularly sensitive but it is possible to import more dangerous species. Around 60 people have licences to keep venomous snakes in England, covering around 300 specimens, and this normally poses no problems although a Nottinghamshire breeder died from a King Cobra bite in 2011[21].
Venomous snakes are available without a licence in continental Europe and are sometimes brought into the U.K.

Peter James's killer in *Love You Dead* (2016) used Saw Scale Vipers to kill some victims and a (non-venomous) Boa Constrictor to choke someone into unconsciousness. The killer also kept Death Stalker scorpions.
Sharon Bolton's *Awakening* (2009) featured a Taipan - a particularly dangerous Australian snake.

The biochemistry of venoms from vertebrates and invertebrates is discussed in detail by Ronald Jenner and Eivind Undheim in their book *Venom*[22].

Radioactive poisons

Radioactive poisons exert their toxic effects through the radiation they emit. Radiation can take the form of fast-moving particles or rays, such as X- or gamma rays. When radiation hits cells it damages them, to the point of destruction if the bombardment is heavy.

Smaller doses of radiation may cause mutations leading to an increased risk of cancer. Depending on the source and type of radiation it can be blocked by a variety of materials - paper in the case of some forms but significant thicknesses of lead or concrete are needed in others. The skin offers some protection against milder forms of radiation but once radioactive material is absorbed by the body it can irradiate sensitive cells at close range. Radioactive materials have half-lives (see the discussion above) and the intensity of radiation declines with time. Half-lives range from fractions of a second to thousands of years and the resulting decay products may, themselves, be radioactive.

The civil use of radioactive materials has caused many fatalities, nearly always by accident. Catherine Caufield's *Multiple Exposures*[23] and Kate Moore's *The Radium Girls: The Dark Story of America's Shining Women*[24] both include graphic accounts of these.

The most notorious criminal use of radioactivity, however, was the deliberate poisoning of Alexander Litvinenko in London in 2006[25]. Russian agents slipped a quantity of the radioisotope polonium-210 into his tea and Litvinenko died three weeks later from radiation sickness. The murderers left a trail of radioactivity across London which took specialists a considerable time to detect and clean up.

Having your killer use a radioactive material to poison someone is not really feasible. Access to these substances is difficult and highly restricted - the polonium-210 used to kill Litvinenko could only have come from a state-run nuclear facility - and a civilian getting hold of some would be at considerable risk of radiation damage through incautious handling. The only possible source of a significantly radioactive material in the community is the radium-containing luminous paint used on old watches and aircraft instruments.

It would be theoretically possible to acquire a number of these devices and scrape off the paint but getting someone to swallow enough would be difficult. Furthermore, they would probably be more likely to die from poisoning by the zinc phosphide base of the paint, which outweighs the radium by approximately 30,000:1, than from the radiation emitted by the radium.

Getting hold of poisons

In Agatha Christie's day it was relatively easy to purchase poisons. Pharmacists stocked a wide range of toxic chemicals which customers could buy for getting rid of pests of various types.

Cyanide was sold for killing wasps, arsenic for flies and rodents and strychnine for a variety of mammalian pests.
Purchasers, who should have been known to the pharmacist, had to sign the poisons book when buying a poison and had

to convince the seller that it was needed for a legitimate reason. Additionally, many medicines, prescribed or sold over the counter as patent cures, contained chemicals dangerous in overdose. Some tightening up took place with the passing of the Pharmacy and Poisons Act 1933 but there were still many strong poisons reasonably readily available.

Traditional pesticides, such as arsenic and cyanide, were gradually superseded by more modern organic* chemicals. After the Second World War a range of new agricultural chemicals came onto the market. Organophosphorus insecticides such as parathion and the demetons were widely used on farms (although not in gardens) and the herbicide paraquat claimed a number of lives in its concentrated form - although a weaker preparation was sold for home gardening. U.K. legislation became tighter and by the 1970s the most toxic agricultural pesticides could only be sold, by licensed sellers, to registered farmers and growers. Restrictions were imposed on organochlorine pesticides such as DDT (which has a low toxicity for humans) because of serious damage caused to the environment.

Many of the more toxic pesticides have now been banned in Britain, on safety or environmental grounds, and some medicines - e.g. strychnine tonics - are no longer used. Chloroform and ether, once sold to the public for removing grease stains from clothing, are no longer available and strychnine, still sold until relatively recently for killing moles, has been banned on animal cruelty grounds.

There has been some relaxation of controls on poisons in the U.K., as part of the Government's deregulation agenda. As a result, some materials, notably concentrated sulfuric acid, became more readily available. Following a spate of acid attacks, and pressure from a number of quarters, the Government increased controls on concentrated sulfuric acid in 2018, requiring anyone purchasing it to hold a licence.

Current controls on poisons are embodied in the Control of Poisons and Explosive Precursors Regulations 2015, amended

* See Glossary

in 2018, which define two groups of substances: regulated and reportable. Would-be purchasers of regulated substances need a licence and photographic ID. A licence is not required to purchase reportable substances but sellers must report any suspicious transactions involving these, or regulated substances, to a national contact point or the police. Sellers must also report any significant losses and thefts of regulated or reportable substances to the police[26].

So how can your intending poisoner get hold of something deadly enough to kill a victim? You cannot buy lethal poisons in high street pharmacies. If you are setting your story in the past it is important to check the legislation in force at the time. For a contemporary setting, however, there is a range of possibilities. Something old found at the back of a shed or medicine cabinet would work - although some substances degrade over time, many would still be lethal a century after the supply date.

Theft is another possibility. Someone working in a hospital, a vet's or a pharmacy would have access to a range of potentially lethal medicines. Stealing them without being discovered is not necessarily straightforward - controlled drugs are kept locked up with strict controls on access and record keeping.

Other drugs, for instance muscle relaxants, are less tightly monitored but if they were discovered to have been used in a murder, anyone with access to them would immediately fall under suspicion.

Burglary, rather than surreptitious pilfering, could be a route in some circumstances although security in hospitals and pharmacies is tight. It may be credible to set a burglary in a small rural veterinary practice where security precautions might be less stringent.

Online pharmacies sell certain medicines containing potentially lethal ingredients, although (usually) not controlled drugs or those only intended for use in hospitals. U.K.-based sites generally require a prescription.

Some overseas sites will supply prescription-only medicines

to buyers in the U.K. though there could be a problem getting them through customs. Travellers to other countries where restrictions are lax can bring back such medicines and may not be challenged on arrival in the U.K.
Poisons have been imported and used for murder and suicide (see case studies in Chapter 2) and poisonous plants are unlikely to be recognised by border force staff - although there are restrictions on importing agricultural plants. It is, of course, illegal to import controlled drugs such as opiates. Undoubtedly there are sources of most poisons on the dark web but amateur poisoners are, in the main, unlikely to know about this.

Many poisons have legitimate industrial or laboratory uses. Someone working in such an establishment could get hold of something lethal but, again, suspicion may fall on them. It may be possible to pose as a legitimate user - there are bona fide reasons for buying potassium cyanide for instance - but few intending poisoners would go to the trouble of setting up a bogus laboratory and obtaining a licence just to eliminate an enemy or dispose of a troublesome relative.

Do-it-yourself methods of acquiring poisons are a possibility if your intending poisoner has some practical experience of chemistry. It would be relatively simple to concentrate the active ingredient in some medicines to lethal levels but synthesising something deadly from scratch would be difficult and require skill, unusual raw materials (which could attract suspicion), and sophisticated equipment. Hydrogen cyanide is an exception - this can be made from unrestricted chemicals but the process would be extremely hazardous in the hands of an amateur.

Various poisonous plants and seeds, such as Castor Bean, Foxglove and Monkshood, are readily available from gardening suppliers or online and it is possible to buy strychnine-containing seeds online. Castor Bean plants are often seen in parks and gardens.

Many poisonous plants, including Deadly Nightshade, Foxglove and even Hemlock, grow wild in the U.K., as do poisonous fungi. Some of these could be used as they are, although getting someone to eat enough of the plants may not be easy as they often have a bitter taste (fungi excepted). It is possible to extract the active ingredients from such plants, with a certain amount of organic chemistry knowledge and skill, but I do not propose to go into details. Attempting to do so can be dangerous - any amateur attempting to extract aconitine from Monkshood for nefarious purposes, for instance, faces a serious risk of self-poisoning unless the correct safety precautions are followed.

Similarly, attempting to extract venoms from animals, vertebrate or invertebrate, would be fraught with difficulty. Experienced herpetologists “milk” venomous snakes in laboratories for the production of antivenoms but they have specialist equipment, thorough training and a ready supply of antidote to hand.

An amateur could well fail fatally in such an endeavour. Trying to extract lethal amounts of venom from spiders or scorpions would also be extremely difficult, not least because the quantities present are very small.

It might be possible to crush, for instance, venomous spiders and use the poison, as is done in the production of cantharidin (Spanish Fly) from beetles, but extracting the venom in an injectable form would be virtually impossible.

Writing poisons (1)

- Poisons can enter the body in various ways and the speed of their effects depends on how they are absorbed.

- Fatal doses vary according to the individual, the form of the poison and how it is administered.

- Some poisons may act in concert with other substances, either aggravating or mitigating their effects.

- Animal venoms can be deadly but getting hold of them may be difficult for a murderer.

- In the U.K. many of the most toxic chemicals are now unavailable to the general public and making them at home, from plants or from other chemicals, is difficult and could be dangerous.

CHAPTER 2: POISONS: SPECIFIC SUBSTANCES

This chapter will outline the effects of particular poisons, with examples, from fact and fiction, of how they have been used.

Abrin

Abrin is a highly toxic protein found in the seeds of the plant *Abrus precatorius*, known as the Rosary Pea, Jequirity Bean and Crab's Eye. The bright red and black seeds have been used in jewellery, rosaries and as weights. Swallowed whole, they may leave the consumer unscathed but, when ground up, the seeds release the poison which can be absorbed. It is considerably more poisonous than ricin (see below) and a lethal dose for humans is estimated at between 5 and 50 micrograms - an extremely small amount[1]. Should your killer consider grinding up the seeds to produce an absorbable poison s/he would need protective clothing since the dust is lethal if inhaled and can also irritate the eyes and skin.

Initial effects are on the gastrointestinal tract. Nausea, vomiting, abdominal pain and bloody diarrhoea appear between a few hours and a few days after abrin is swallowed[2]. As the chemical is absorbed slowly, washing out the stomach may remove enough of the material to prevent fatal results. There is no specific antidote to abrin so, if washing out fails, supportive care and pain relief is the only therapy. If a fatal dose has been ingested, death is likely to occur within a few days from multi-organ failure.

Case study: Abrin purchase[3]

In November 2014 a British woman, Kuntal Patel, was jailed for three years for buying abrin from a US source via the dark web. She was originally charged with the attempted murder of her mother but the jury believed her when she claimed she had bought the poison to kill herself. She was caught when US agents arrested the dealer, posed as him and informed the U.K. authorities when Patel attempted to buy a second batch. She was prosecuted under the Biological Weapons Act 1974 which prohibits the development, production, acquisition and possession of certain biological agents, toxins and biological weapons.

Aconitine

Known as the queen of poisons because of its lethality, aconitine is an extremely poisonous material with an estimated lethal dose for humans of one to two milligrams[4]. It is found, along with several similar compounds, in a number of plants in the *Aconitum* genus of which *Aconitum napellus* -Monkshood or Wolfsbane - is the most familiar. Other members of the genus, notably *Aconitum ferox* are more toxic.

When taken into the mouth, aconitine has an extremely bitter taste and produces a burning sensation on the tongue, which is why accidental poisoning by Monkshood is unusual, even through the plant is common in the wild and in gardens. Swallowed aconitine produces its initial effects within 20 minutes to two hours.

These include tingling, numbness in the face and limbs, sweating and nausea. Muscle weakness develops along with chest pain, vomiting, diarrhoea and irregular heartbeat. Eventually the heart stops and the victim dies[5]. Aconitine can be absorbed through the skin but fatal poisoning is unlikely (the reported case of a gardener dying after brushing against Monkshood cannot be attributed to aconitine) although an unpleasant tingling and numbness may occur.

Aconitine has no current medical uses in the U.K. although it was used in the past - Agatha Christie featured it in *The 4:50 from Paddington* (1957). (In the United States, it was published at the same time under the title *What Mrs McGillicuddy Saw!*, the publisher was Dodd Mead. The change of title was because of belief that the American audience would not know the names of British railway stations.)

Some Chinese medical practitioners still use extracts of aconitine-bearing plants for a variety of purposes. It has no antidote and supportive therapy is the only option once a charcoal washout has removed any traces from the stomach. If the patient survives for 24 hours they are likely to recover[6].

Case study: A killer curry[7]

> In 2010 Lakhvir Kaur Singh was found guilty at the Old Bailey of murdering her ex-lover, Lakhvinder Cheema, and causing grievous bodily harm to his fiancee after she added aconite to a curry which the couple ate. Shortly after eating the food, Mr Cheema started vomiting, experienced stomach pains and suffered numbness, paralysis and loss of vision. He died four hours later and his fiancée spent three days in a coma before recovering. Singh, who had imported the poison in the form of *Aconitum ferox* from India, was given a life sentence with a 23 year minimum term.

Arsenic

Once known as "Poudre de succession" (inheritance powder), arsenic has been used for dispatching enemies and the inconvenient for centuries. It is a semi-metallic element which is only moderately hazardous in its uncombined form. When reacted with oxygen, to form arsenic trioxide (white arsenic), it is lethal. Medicinally, it has been used as a tonic and for treating syphilis. Arsenic compounds have also been used for cosmetic purposes, as herbicides and for killing flies and rodents. Green arsenic compounds were used as dyes and pigments for wallpaper, sometimes resulting in harmful exposure to people nearby. Most of these uses have been discontinued or tightly restricted although arsenic compounds are still in use as pesticides in parts of Asia. It is no longer possible to buy arsenic at the local pharmacy.

As a poison, arsenic has usually been used as the trioxide. Since it is tasteless, adding it to food and drink has been the favoured approach. Depending on the dose and rate of ingestion it will produce either acute or chronic symptoms. A large dose will cause severe stomach pain, and vomiting, easily mistaken for gastritis, within thirty minutes. Copious diarrhoea will follow and, as the poison disrupts a wide range of bodily processes, blood pressure drops and the skin becomes clammy. Within a few hours, death occurs from circulatory failure. Vomiting may eject sufficient of the poison to prevent death but if 100-

150 milligrams are absorbed the victim is likely to die[8].

Arsenic is a cumulative poison - it builds up in the body if it is absorbed at a faster rate than it is (slowly) excreted. Repeated doses thus lead to chronic poisoning, characterised by nausea, vomiting, dizziness, cramp and developing paralysis. Death occurs when vital organs simply shut down. Signs of chronic arsenic poisoning include white lines across the nails, darkening skin and scaly patches appearing on the palms and soles of the feet[9].

Murder by arsenic is uncommon now that restrictions have been imposed on its sale in most countries. However there have been some arsenic killings in the U.S. in relatively recent years.

- In 2007 a woman was convicted of killing her husband with arsenic, albeit on circumstantial evidence;[10]
- In 1968 a Georgia woman was convicted of killing five members of her family with arsenic in order to claim life insurance[11];
- In 1982 a woman from Alabama was convicted of killing her husband and poisoning one of her children[12];
- and in 1984 a woman from North Carolina was executed for killing one person with arsenic although she confessed to killing four others[13].

Agatha Christie used arsenic a number of times, notably in *Murder is Easy* (1939). For a range of historical cases, see *A is for Arsenic* by Kathryn Harkup and James C. Whorton's *The Arsenic Century*[14].

Atropine

Atropine is one of several toxic chemicals found in the Belladonna, or Deadly Nightshade, plant *Atropa belladonna.* This plant, and some of its near relatives, is one of the more common causes of plant poisoning requiring medical treatment but once the symptoms have been diagnosed correctly, treatment is effective. Poisoning by atropine is quite distinctive and is characterised by the memory-jogging mantra "hot as a hare, blind as a bat, dry as a bone, red as a beetroot and mad as a hatter." Atropine, in dangerous amounts, sends the body tem-

perature up. It also dilates the pupils of the eye (useful for ophthalmic examinations and for beauty enhancement, it is said) hence vision is blurred. The workings of the salivary glands are suppressed, hence the dryness in the mouth and the dilation of the near-surface blood vessels gives the skin a bright red colour. Atropine causes confusion, slurred speech and hallucinations, hence the reference to madness[15].
The ease by which its symptoms can be recognised and treated makes atropine less suitable as a murder weapon than its high toxicity would suggest (about 100mg is likely to be fatal to an adult)[16]. Furthermore, it is very bitter to the taste and is not easy to get hold of in the pure state although some chemical and medical laboratories may use it.

Most of the atropine currently in stock is in the form of injections to be used in case of nerve agent poisoning (see below). It is an ingredient of belladonna plasters, used for pain relief, but extracting it from the product for illicit use would be difficult.

Case study: A toxic tonic[17]

Paul Agutter, an Edinburgh lecturer, wanted to be rid of his wife but simply leaving or divorcing her would have cost him too much money. Instead, he decided to murder her with atropine, which he stole from the university where he worked. He added the poison to several tonic water bottles and put most of them back on the shelf of the supermarket where he bought them, not realising that he had been seen by a student at his university who subsequently reported Agutter's behaviour to the police. He retained a bottle which had a larger dose of atropine in it than those he returned and used this to mix his wife a gin and tonic. Fortunately for her, the flavours in the drink did not disguise the bitterness of the atropine and she drank only half of it. Agutter left a message on the GP's answering machine, not expecting it to be picked up, but a locum heard it, came round to the Agutters' and called an ambulance. Mrs Agutter survived, although she was seriously ill for some days, and ten other people were hospitalised after drinking the returned tonic. Agutter was sentenced to 12 years for attempted murder.

Deadly Nightshade itself could be used by your killer to murder someone although the bitterness would still be a problem. The berries resemble edible soft fruits so they could be incorporated into a smoothie or pie, with copious amounts of sugar. The victim would have to be kept away from medical help for several hours if their life was not to be saved. Atropine and related compounds are found in the plant *Datura stramonium* (Thornapple or Jimson Weed). This was used by Ruth Rendell in her short story *Thornapple* (1982).

Botulinum toxin

One of the most poisonous substances known to science is in widespread use on many high streets by people who are not trained chemists or toxicologists. It can also be bought online. This is botulinum toxin, full scientific name onabotulinumtoxinA and trade name Botox, used in cosmetic clinics to smooth out wrinkles.

The toxin is produced by the bacterium *Clostridium botulinum* which is responsible for botulism, a type of food poisoning caused by improperly treated canned food. It can also occur when wounds are infected by spores and sometimes develops in the gut of infants. Spores of the bacterium may be present in honey which is why this food should not be given to infants under 12 months old.

Botulinum toxin is ferociously poisonous. There are eight types and the lethal dose by injection of type H is estimated to be two billionths of a gram (two nanograms)[18]. Type A, the form used medically and cosmetically, is less toxic with an estimated injected fatal dose of 50 nanograms[19]. The amounts used in cosmetic preparations cannot easily be compared with toxicity data because the manufacturer uses a specific technique for measuring the potency of its products. Nevertheless, a rough estimate suggests that the contents of a couple of vials of cosmetic botulinum toxin A would be lethal if injected into a vein - assuming the attacker could keep the victim still enough, of course. Botulinum toxin is supplied in vials as a dry powder which has to be mixed with a saline solution before use and then kept in the fridge, since its potency declines over time.

The toxin blocks the nerve impulses which control the muscles, causing paralysis. This property has widespread medical uses in treating conditions caused by muscle spasms.

Its effects are localised but there is a risk that they could spread beyond the intended site and cause problems. Symptoms of botulinum poisoning include drooping eyelids, dry mouth, difficulty in swallowing, general muscle weakness and problems in breathing which can ultimately be fatal[20].

It is treatable if medical attention is received in time although fatalities from botulinum food poisoning have occurred in the U.K. and elsewhere. Botulinum toxin does not appear to have been used as a murder weapon although there have been some reported deaths attributed to overdoses during its medical use[21].

In summer 2018 it was announced that a U.K. cosmetics and toiletries chain was proposing to offer botox treatments in store by "trained staff". This will clearly increase the amount of this material in the community.

Carbon monoxide
Carbon monoxide is a highly poisonous gas which forms when fuels containing carbon (coal, oil, gas, petrol, wood etc.) burn in insufficient oxygen. It kills by binding to the haemoglobin in the red blood cells, preventing it from carrying oxygen from the lungs to the tissues so the body effectively suffocates from within. Symptoms start with headache, dizziness and nausea followed by unconsciousness, coma and death[22].

Carbon monoxide poisoning is treatable if caught in time but can result in brain damage. The skin of someone poisoned with carbon monoxide would look very pink as the compound formed between haemoglobin and carbon monoxide (carboxyhaemoglobin) is bright red[23].

For a long time carbon monoxide was a major component of the town gas supplied to homes for lighting, heating and cooking. It was used as a means of suicide - the poet Sylvia Plath killed herself by putting her head in an unlit gas oven - but the intro-

duction of natural gas removed this option.
The other former means of suicide by carbon monoxide was to run a car engine in a closed garage or to connect the exhaust to the cabin with a hose. Older cars, especially with the choke operating, produced significant concentrations of carbon monoxide in the exhaust but modern vehicles have catalytic converters which remove most of the gas once they are warmed up. The residual gas can still kill, however, but it takes longer.
A would-be murderer would need to drug or otherwise subdue the victims beforehand if they were not to realise what was happening.

Case study: The deadly dentist[24]

> In 2010 a Northern Irish dentist, Dr Colin Howell, pleaded guilty to the 1991 murder of his wife and an RUC police officer, Trevor Buchanan, with whose wife Howell had conducted an affair. The couple were found dead in Howell's car with a vacuum cleaner hose running from the exhaust to the front seats. Originally the deaths were thought to be suicide but the investigation was reopened and Howell was arrested in 2009. He had gassed his wife by connecting a garden hose to the car exhaust and running it into the bedroom where he held it close to her face until she died. He put her body in the car and drove to Constable Buchanan's house where he repeated the procedure. Both victims struggled as he gassed them. With the two bodies in his car, he drove to a garage behind his late father-in-law's house and set up the scene to look like suicide. The police were criticised for overlooking evidence which would have contradicted the suicide theory.

Poorly maintained heating appliances and blocked flues can cause a build-up of carbon monoxide in houses as the carbon in the fuel cannot burn completely to carbon dioxide. This has caused many cases of, often fatal, poisoning and is why a carbon monoxide alarm, and adequate ventilation, in the home is so important. Deliberate tampering with heating systems has been used in crime novels including Rachel Abbott's *Sleep Tight*

(2014).

Using a smouldering barbecue in a tent has sometimes caused carbon monoxide poisoning in campers.

Carbon monoxide is used in industry and laboratories in cylinders but is not normally sold to the general public. In one case a university lecturer borrowed a cylinder of the gas from the stores and poisoned his wife in their caravan, taking a dose himself to make it look as if a faulty gas fire was to blame. The excessively high level of the gas in his wife's blood alerted the forensic team and the killer was arrested and convicted[25]. A more ingenious method was used by an anaesthetist in Hong Kong in 2015. He put a yoga ball full of carbon monoxide in a car carrying his wife and daughter. As the ball deflated the gas escaped and killed them both[26].

Chlorine

Chlorine is a greenish-yellow, highly toxic gas which was used on the battlefield during the first world war and has also been used against civilians in the Middle East. Low concentrations of the gas in air irritate the nose and lungs but as the concentration increases chest pain, coughing and shortness of breath develop. Higher concentrations, and longer exposure times, cause the lungs to become inflamed and fill up with fluid (pulmonary oedema)[27].

A large dose of chlorine will kill in a few minutes. There is no antidote but supportive therapy can help if given in time. People whose lungs are already impaired, such as smokers, are more vulnerable to the effects of the gas.

Numerous incidents involving the use of chlorine have occurred, some of them fatal. Examples include industrial accidents, leaks of liquefied chlorine during transport and, commonly, the mixing of chemicals leading to the generation of the gas. Cleaning products containing bleach release chlorine when acidic chemicals, such as toilet cleaners, are added to them. In a confined space this can be dangerous, if not deadly.

Case study: (Nearly) kicking the bucket[28]

> In 2017 a woman in Sheffield was rushed to hospital when she mixed three different cleaning products and hot water in a bucket. Shortly after starting to mop the floor she developed chest pains and was taken by ambulance to hospital where she was given oxygen. She made a full recovery but could have been seriously harmed.

For a graphic account of the effects of chlorine in war, see Wilfred Owen's poem *Dulce et Decorum Est* (c1917).

Cyanide
Cyanide is, chemically, an ion - a carbon atom connected to a nitrogen atom and bearing a negative charge. It is always found combined with something else - sodium and potassium cyanides are white crystals while hydrogen cyanide is a gas which dissolves in water to form prussic acid. The solids are odourless and tasteless whereas the gas and solution smell of bitter almonds, although half the population cannot detect the smell[29].

Adding sodium or potassium cyanide to an acid releases hydrogen cyanide gas, which is the basis of the U.S. gas chamber. The same thing happens when one of these chemicals is swallowed and reacts with stomach acids. Hydrogen cyanide in the victim's breath causes it to smell of bitter almonds and sniffing it too deeply is not recommended. A cadaver poisoned with cyanide is a dangerous thing. If this is suspected as a cause of death the post-mortem would be carried out in a special room with ventilation that traps the fumes and with the pathologist using respiratory protection. In a case covered by a B.B.C. TV documentary a scientist killed herself with a cyanide compound, using just enough to achieve the desired effect without putting the pathologist at risk[30].

Cyanide works by blocking the action of an enzyme involved in using energy within the cells.

Oxygen is carried to the tissues by the blood but cannot be used so the blood in the veins remains bright red. This is why the skin of cyanide poisoning victims may appear pink and flushed. It is a common mistake to describe them as looking blue - the condition cyanosis (blueness) refers to the colour not the chemical and can be caused by other poisons. Around 50mg of cyanide is regarded as a lethal dose although some people can tolerate considerably more[31].

Cyanide is very quick to act. Symptoms occur after one to fifteen minutes[32] depending on what is in the stomach at the time. Injected or inhaled cyanide acts very quickly.

Victims gasp for breath, feel weak, may have seizures and collapse. They fall into a coma and eventually breathing and the heart stop. Large doses can kill within minutes although some victims last longer[33]. There are antidotes to cyanide but they have to be administered almost immediately to prevent death. Laboratories and industrial premises handling these compounds are equipped with kits for the rapid injection of antidotes.

Cyanide is a favourite of Golden Age mystery writers and Agatha Christie used it in fourteen of her stories. In those days it was possible to buy cyanide at a pharmacy, for controlling pests, and diluted prussic acid was even used in some toiletries[34]. Nowadays its supply is tightly restricted although someone able to demonstrate a legitimate use for a cyanide compound can purchase it from a specialist supplier.

In real life there have been many cyanide poisonings throughout history. The most horrific was the mass suicide of 909 followers of the cult leader Jim Jones in 1978. Before shooting himself he persuaded his victims to swallow a soft drink laced with cyanide which rapidly killed them.

More recently, a Japanese woman dubbed the “Black Widow” was sentenced to death for murdering three men, including her husband, and attempting to murder another by poisoning them with cyanide[35].

Case study: A terminal headache[36]

> Inspired by the 1982 tampering of Tylenol tablets in Chicago, which killed seven people through cyanide poisoning, Stella Nickell of Auburn, Washington, used a similar ploy to get rid of her husband. She added cyanide to migraine tablets and planted three bottles on a supermarket shelf, retaining some for use on her spouse. He duly swallowed four tablets to deal with a headache, collapsed and died in hospital shortly after. Initially, the cause of death was thought to be emphysema but someone else bought a bottle of the contaminated tablets and died as a result. Her autopsy revealed death from cyanide. When this was reported in the press Stella Nickell came forward, claiming her husband had died in the same way, hoping that the authorities would blame an unknown product-tamperer. It didn't work and she received a 90-year jail sentence.

Cyanide-containing compounds are present naturally in a variety of plants. Crushing laurel leaves releases small quantities of hydrogen cyanide and butterfly collectors used this in their killing bottles in days past. The pips and kernels of a range of fruits contain chemicals called cyanogenic glycosides which release cyanide in the digestive tract up to two hours of swallowing them. The seeds have to be chewed first otherwise they are likely to pass thorough without causing harm.

Poisoning someone with apricot kernels, which contain about two mg of cyanide each, would be very difficult although if your killer was a skilled chemist it may be feasible for them to concentrate the toxic components. It is possible to buy apricot kernels and a derivative of them, laetrile, online.

Laetrile is spurious treatment for cancer which has made some people money and others rather ill. It is banned by the U.S. Food and Drug Administration as it doesn't work and is dangerous. There have been several cases of cyanide poisoning from fruit kernel and laetrile ingestion[37,38] so this is a possible means of murder. Getting the victim to eat enough, however, could be problematic unless they are gullible and could be persuaded that they are taking a healthy food supplement. Such people exist.

Digitalis

Digitalis is the generic name for foxglove plants of which *Digitalis purpurea*, with its striking purple flowers, is the most familiar. Foxgloves are highly poisonous and can be found both in the wild and on sale in garden centres.

Digitalis is also the name for the plant-based heart medicine which was used before its active ingredients were purified and standardised. Foxgloves contain a mixture of several different alkaloids, of varying toxicity. Two of these, digitoxin and digoxin, have saved the lives of thousands of patients with heart disease.

Digitoxin is the main active ingredient of digitalis and is much more toxic than digoxin. It also has a longer half-life in the body[39] which can make safe treatment difficult. Purified digoxin replaced digitalis and digitoxin although the use of digoxin has declined because of concerns about adverse reactions in some patients. Safer drugs are now available.

Digitalis works by making the action of the heart muscle stronger and stabilising it by suppressing excess electrical activity when the heart is fluttering[40]. An overdose will stop the heart quickly and completely. Symptoms of digitalis poisoning include nausea, vomiting, diarrhoea, visual disturbances and either slowing or speeding up the heart depending on the dose and the individual. Digoxin affects the heart within seconds if injected but takes longer if swallowed[41].

Digitalis and digoxin have caused many accidental poisonings, either through people inadvertently consuming the plant or through poor digoxin manufacturing procedures[42]. In fiction Agatha Christie used digitalis as a murder weapon in *Appointment With Death* (1938) and, in real life, digoxin was used the serial killer Charles Cullen, a nurse who confessed to killing 40 patients in New Jersey and Pennsylvania between 1988 and 2003[43]

Case study: Suicide by Foxglove[44]

In 2004 Michael O'Connor, a British amateur botanist, killed himself with a lethal dose of digitalis by eating Foxglove leaves. Although he then cut his wrists with a gardening knife, the wounds were superficial and it was the digitalis that killed him. He was taken to hospital, in Sheffield, but the staff were unable to save him.

DNP

DNP stands for dinitrophenol (more correctly 2,4-dinitrophenol), a chemical which has been used as a pesticide in the past. It is currently used, against medical advice, as a slimming pill and therein lies a problem since it is highly toxic. DNP disrupts the smooth processing of energy in our cells so that it is released far too quickly and cannot be used by bodily processes. It's a bit like running a car engine at maximum revs for a prolonged period while stationary. Like the car engine, the body overheats. This burns up fat, which is why the pills, bought online from abroad, are used by slimmers, but it can cause serious damage.

Between 2007 and 2016 DNP was mentioned on U.K. death certificates 15 times[45] and there have been other cases since. In 2018 an online steroid dealer, who supplied DNP to a woman who died as a result, was convicted of manslaughter[46].

Case study: Slimming pill fatality [47,48]

In 2017 an abused young woman on home leave from a psychiatric unit overdosed on DNP pills, bought online from eastern Europe. Her heart rate shot up to 190 beats per minute and she was breathing twice as fast as normal[47]. Although she told paramedics what she had taken, she was not treated as a priority and was not seen by a doctor for an hour and a half. The doctor did not know what DNP was and didn't seek advice. She died three and a half hours after admission. The coroner found that care at the overwhelmed A&E department was inadequate.

Fungi
Foraging for fungi is a popular pastime but it can have tragic consequences if the wrong species are picked and eaten. Many fungi are perfectly safe to eat but some, particularly those in the genus *Amanita*, are deadly. Death Cap, Destroying Angel - the clue is in the names.

These mushrooms, which are easily mistaken for edible species, contain a range of toxic compounds of which the amatoxins, particularly alpha- amanitin, are the most poisonous. They have a pleasant taste and their toxic properties are not destroyed by cooking. The mushrooms do not have an immediate effect. Once a fatal quantity is swallowed, vomiting, nausea and stomach pains develop after a few hours. In many cases the patient may seem to recover but this is illusory since the poisons are busily attacking the liver and damaging the kidneys. Jaundice and coma appear a few days later, as the liver is destroyed, and the patient dies four to seven days afterwards.[49] If a small dose is absorbed the patient may recover with supportive treatment. Washing out the stomach before the toxins are absorbed can help, as can penicillin G in some cases. With large doses the only effective treatment is a liver transplant. Half a Death Cap mushroom can be fatal.

Case study: Somerset Death Cap[50, 51]

In 2013 Christina Hale gathered some mushrooms from her garden in Bridgwater, Somerset, and made soup which she ate for her evening meal. Her husband also had some and the following day both were struck down with vomiting and diarrhoea which persisted all night. Next morning the GP was called who diagnosed norovirus and gave Mrs Hale an anti-emetic after which she felt a little better. This didn't last long and at around midnight she was rushed to hospital where her heart stopped on several occasions. She died of multiple organ failure four days after eating the Death Cap mushrooms in her soup[51]. Her husband, who had eaten much less of the soup, survived.

"Destroying Angel" was the title of an episode of *Midsomer*

Murders[a] in which the fungus was used to murder someone and Ruth Rendell used Death Cap in the short story *Shreds and Slivers* (1995). Death Cap and Destroying Angel are fairly common in the U.K.

Although their effects are not usually lethal it is worth mentioning two fungi which can have a dramatic effect on the human body when combined with alcohol. The Common Ink Cap (*Coprinopsis atramentaria*) and the Shaggy Ink Cap (*Coprinus comatus*) contain a substance which prevents the body breaking alcohol down completely.

Indeed, the former is known as Tippler's Bane because of its potency in this respect while the latter is less powerful and does not always produce serious symptoms. Someone eating Common Ink Cap within a few hours of drinking alcohol will suffer nausea and vomiting, palpitations, reddening of the face and tingling in the limbs[52]. The effects are similar to the drug disulfiram (Antabuse) which is given to alcoholics to discourage drinking. Ruth Rendell used this phenomenon in the short story *Means of Evil* (1979).

Gelsemium

In November 2012 the Russian exile Alexander Perepilichny went for a jog near his Surrey home, collapsed and died. Initial medical opinion was that he had died of heart failure but traces of gelsemine, a highly toxic chemical present in the plant *Gelsemium elegans* and its relatives, were reported in his stomach[53]. Subsequently, the botanist who identified the gelsemine changed her testimony.

The initial findings of gelsemine traces prompted suspicions that he had been poisoned because of his whistleblowing on organised crime in his home country. Furthermore, it was reported in 2017 that U.S. intelligence told MI6 that the Kremlin had ordered his assassination[54]. How true this is has not been established, and maybe never will be, but the inquest into his death was repeatedly delayed, partly because of the possible involvement of the security services. The coroner finally recorded a verdict of natural causes in December 2018[55] but suspicions remain - it is reported that gelsemine was produced in a special poisons laboratory run by the Russian secret service[56].

Gelsemium is a genus of plants all parts of which are highly toxic. In the U.S. *Gelsemium sempervirens*, known as Yellow or Carolina Jessamine, has caused a number of poisonings, possibly including people who have eaten honey produced from its nectar[57]. The Asian plant *Gelsemium elegans* is known as Heartbreak Grass and has been used as a murder weapon in China and Russia for many years. Symptoms of *Gelsemium* poisoning include drooping eyelids and lower jaw, severe feebleness as the muscles relax, convulsions and respiratory paralysis. A dose of 35mg could be fatal to humans[58].

Agatha Christie used Yellow Jasmine to kill a character in The Big Four (1927) and gelsemine was used to kill a journalist in season five of *House of Cards*[b].

Case study: Poisoned cat stew[59]

Chinese billionaire Long Liyuan sat down to lunch in December 2011 with Huang Guang, a Guangdong local government official whose corruption he intended to expose. Three people ate a cat stew at the luncheon and were hospitalised but only Long Liyuan died. Police believed that the official put *Gelsemium elegans* in the stew to kill Long Liyuan, eating some himself to divert suspicion. Huang Guang was arrested, convicted of murder and sentenced to death.

Getting hold of these plants is likely to be a problem for your poisoner unless he or she visits the southern U.S., Central America, or south-east Asia (or has a friend in the F.S.B.!). Small amounts could be smuggled in, perhaps as seeds or cuttings. Amazingly, the seeds of *Gelsemium sempervirens* can be bought online and could be grown in a greenhouse. Homeopathic Gelsemium preparations are non-toxic as there is virtually nothing there.

Hemlock

Hemlock is familiar to many as the poison with which the Greek philosopher Socrates was executed. There are three types of poisonous plants bearing this name: Spotted Hemlock (Conium maculatum); Water Hemlock (*Cicuta maculata* and *Cicuta virosa*) and Hemlock Water Dropwort (*Oenanthe crocata*). All are potentially deadly but different toxic components are involved.

Spotted Hemlock contains the toxin coniine which Agatha Christie used in the story *Five Little Pigs* (1942). It acts on the nervous system and paralyses the muscles. Symptoms of coniine poisoning, which can start within 20 minutes, include excessive salivation, vomiting in some cases, dilation of the pupils and rapid heartbeat. Paralysis starts at the feet and moves upwards until it fatally affects the heart and lungs[60]. Coniine did have some medical uses but was discontinued owing to the narrow gap between a useful dose and a toxic one. An estimated fatal dose of coniine for humans is 100-130mg[61].

Water Hemlock contains, among other things, the poison cicutoxin. This also acts on the nervous system but in a different way. Symptoms resemble coniine to begin with - salivation, vomiting, dilated pupils - but these are followed by convulsions, seizures, coma and death[62]. Cicutoxin has no medical uses.

Hemlock Water Dropwort contains oenanthotoxin and has been described as possibly the most poisonous British plant[63]. Oenanthotoxin is another neurotoxin with no medical uses and is contained in all parts of the plant. The roots of Hemlock Water Dropwort, which contain the highest concentration of the toxin, resemble a bunch of whitish carrots and are known as dead man's fingers[64].

There have been many accidental poisonings and deaths from these plants. Spotted Hemlock is sometimes mistaken for wild parsley and the roots of Water Hemlock and Hemlock Water Dropwort are sometimes mis-identified as parsnips.
The U.S. Center for Disease Control reports that deaths have been associated with children using Water Hemlock stems as toy whistles [65].

Case study: Death in Maine[66]

Two brothers were foraging for wild ginseng in Maine woods in 1992 when one of them collected Water Hemlock by mistake. He took three bites out of the root and within half an hour vomited and began to have convulsions. Despite paramedics arriving within 15 minutes and rushing him to hospital, he died three hours later. His brother, who had only taken one bite, developed seizures and delirium but survived after gastric lavage and supportive care were provided.

From your murderer's point of view, hemlock is a useful poison. It can be disguised as food, doesn't have the overwhelmingly bitter taste of some poisonous plants and is relatively common - Spotted Hemlock grows on waste ground and Water Hemlock in wet areas. *Cicuta maculata* is the North American species: in the U.K. the - also highly poisonous - *Cicuta virosa* grows[67].

Someone with reasonable botanical knowledge should be able to procure it with diligent searching and a GP or A&E doctor may not recognise either coniine or cicutoxin poisoning. Hemlock plants do not appear to have been used for murder in recent years but in 2006 a gardener in Devon chopped up Spotted Hemlock leaves and swallowed them with an alcoholic drink in a bid to commit suicide. It worked[68].

Insulin

Insulin is a classic example of Paracelsus's dictum: in small amounts it is a remedy but in larger amounts it is a poison. Crime writers, and some would-be murderers, have thought of insulin as an ideal murder weapon since it is present naturally in the body and was thought to be undetectable. This may have been the case once but modern analytical methods, including the measurements of insulin at the injection site and other compounds in body fluids, can indicate when insulin poisoning has probably occurred, provided that the proper precautions are taken with samples.

Professor Vincent Marks, an acknowledged expert on insulin, has stated that insulin "is an inefficient and ineffective weapon, largely because of the length of time it takes to cause death and the ease with which it can be diagnosed and treated"[69]. Blood glucose normally has to stay dangerously low for more than 12 hours if death is to ensue[70].

All cells in the body use glucose, derived from food, as fuel. For the brain it is the only fuel whereas other tissues can use fats as well. Too much glucose in the blood is bad for the brain and too little can also be dangerous. Insulin is responsible for keeping the delicate balance between too much and too little and if it is given in excess, by injection for instance, it can cause glucose levels to plummet, leading to coma and death. If detected in time, this hypoglycaemic coma can be reversed although brain damage can occur if it has gone on too long.

Murders and murder-suicides involving insulin have occurred and there have also been cases of attempted murder and assault[71]. Injecting a fit adult with a substantial amount of insulin against their will, and keeping them away from medical treatment long enough for it to kill them, would be difficult. Children, infirm adults and people in hospital are more feasible targets and there are numerous cases of actual or attempted attacks on these groups.

Insulin Murders, by Vincent Marks and Caroline Richmond[72], provides a comprehensive account of cases involving insulin before 2007. More recently, a pharmacist was jailed in 2018 for using insulin to subdue his wife before strangling her[73]

Case study: Murder on the ward[74]

Beverley Allitt was a nurse working on the children's ward of a Lincolnshire hospital. Between February and April1991 she murdered four children, two of them with insulin, and attempted to murder three others. At her trial in 1993 she was also convicted of grievous bodily harm on six other children who survived her attacks, some of which involved insulin. She received thirteen concurrent life sentences and was believed to be suffering from Munchausen's Syndrome by Proxy. It was only after the fourth child died that suspicions were raised. Investigations showed that Allitt was on duty when all the incidents happened and also had access to the drugs used.

Muscle relaxants

Muscle relaxants, as their name implies, relax the muscles and have two main categories of use. The first is in the treatment of muscle pain - diazepam is often prescribed for this purpose - and the second is in surgical practice.

Surgical muscle relaxants (neuromuscular blockers) are used when someone needs to be intubated - having a tube passed down their trachea to maintain an airway during emergency treatment or surgery. An injection paralyses the muscles within a minute so that the tube can be inserted smoothly and without resistance.

Neuromuscular blockers are used alongside general anaesthetics to relax muscles, making surgery easier for the surgeon and less painful for the patient on waking. By using these drugs anaesthetists can use less general anaesthetic, thus reducing the risk to the patient[75].

The original surgical muscle relaxant was tubocurarine, based on South American arrow poisons. More modern versions, such as succinylcholine (also known as suxamethonium), pancuronium, rocuronium and vecuronium, are more effective and precise in their actions. These are not stocked in high street pharmacies and are only used by fully trained professionals. Used maliciously they would cause fatal paralysis of the lungs, leading to suffocation.

During the 1960s succinylcholine was regarded by some as the perfect poison. It breaks down quickly in the body to compounds which occur naturally and it was thought to be undetectable at a post mortem. Modern analytical techniques, however, can detect it and its metabolite, succinylmonocholine[76].

Injected into a vein, 80mg of succinylcholine will relax a 70kg person's muscles within a minute[77] although a would-be murderer would probably use a larger dose which may act slightly faster. As the drug takes effect, movement of the eyes and fingers becomes difficult, followed by paralysis of the arms and legs. Breathing becomes a struggle and eventually unconsciousness occurs. When the muscles of the chest are finally paralysed, breathing stops and death ensues. In the medical context, where respiratory support is provided, the effects of the drug wear off in 5-15 minutes but that is of little comfort to a dead poisoning victim. A particularly terrifying aspect of poisoning by this group of drugs is that, until they pass out, victims are awake and aware of what is happening but cannot move.

Case study: A poisoned politician[78]

Kathy Augustine was a prominent Nevada politician and in July 2006 she was found unconscious at her home. Three days later she died in hospital, the cause of death being ascribed to a heart attack. A few days later her husband, Chaz Higgs, came to the authorities' attention when he attempted suicide by slitting his wrists. It was only when police talked to a colleague of Higgs, at the hospital where he worked as a nurse, that suspicions were raised. Higgs had remarked, on hearing of a murder by stabbing, that the way to get rid of someone was to inject them with succinylcholine as it couldn't be traced at autopsy.
Police then had Augustine's urine sample analysed and succinylcholine and its metabolites were found, despite the fact that the hospital had not administered the drug. Higgs had access to succinylcholine at work and, despite legal arguments that the amounts present were just a trace, the jury convicted him of murder

In fiction, succinylcholine has been used to kill - it featured in an episode of *Taggart*[c] - and Jonathan Moore used vecuronium in his novel *The Poison Artist* (2016).

Nerve agents

Many drugs and poisons act on the nerves but, following the Wiltshire poisonings (see below), the term is commonly used to refer to a group of chemicals called anticholinesterase compounds. Chemically, they are usually organophosphorus compounds and range in toxicity from garden insecticides, formerly sold over the counter, to some of the most toxic compounds devised. A description of how they work is included in the box below but you do not need the details to appreciate their lethality.

How nerve agents work

> Nerves carry messages in the form of electrical impulses and the junction of two nerves is called a synapse. As an impulse passes across the synapse a chemical called acetylcholine is formed. A new message cannot pass until this chemical is removed and an enzyme called acetylcholinesterase does the job of breaking it down. If this enzyme is inhibited by an anticholinesterase compound the acetylcholine remains and the nerves can no longer function. This has serious implications for many bodily processes and can lead to death.

Nerve agents - previously known as nerve gases although they are generally liquids - were developed for military use and a range of organophosphorus pesticides appeared almost as a sideline. With the exception of sarin, which was used by a terrorist group in an attack on the Tokyo underground in 1995 (see case study below), these military chemicals will only be used by nation states or their agents. Manufacturing them is difficult and highly dangerous - the person doing so would need considerable chemistry skills, sophisticated equipment and 100% effective protective clothing. If you are writing a spy thriller with a secret service or well-funded terrorist group involved it may be feasible to use one of these compounds. Otherwise they are not really credible in a crime novel.

Case study: Sarin underground[79]

> On 20th March 1995 members of the cult Aum Shinryko released the nerve agent sarin on three lines of the Tokyo subway. The liquid material was transported in plastic bags which were dropped on the train floors and punctured, allowing the sarin to evaporate. Twelve people were killed, 50 were seriously injured (some dying later) and 1,000 other people suffered temporary vision problems.

Nerve agents may be inhaled if dispersed as a vapour cloud, as in Tokyo, and are also readily absorbed through the skin. Symptoms of organophosphorus poisoning include pinpoint pupils, tightness in the chest, foaming at the mouth, nausea, vomiting, loss of bowel and bladder control, convulsions, coma and death. They can be countered by an injection of atropine and one of a group of drugs called oximes - pralidoxime is one of these. Troops in combat where they are likely to encounter chemical attacks carry injectable supplies of these drugs.

Sarin has been used militarily in Iraq and VX is also reported to have been used in Angola. VX, a droplet (10mg) of which is likely to prove fatal if inhaled or absorbed through the skin, was used to assassinate one person by the group behind the Tokyo subway attack. It was also said to be used in the killing of Kim Jong-nam in Kuala Lumpur airport in 2017[80]. In the latter case it is likely that it was used as a binary weapon where two less-toxic components are mixed on the target, producing the lethal compound.

The most notorious nerve agents are the group of chemicals known as Novichok. Developed by the former Soviet Union in the 1970s and 1980s these are more toxic than VX and came to prominence following the poisoning of Sergei and Yulia Skripal in Salisbury in March 2018 (see case study below).

Case study: Novichok in Wiltshire[81]

On 4th March 2018 Sergei and Yulia Skripal were poisoned with the nerve agent Novichok in the Wiltshire town of Salisbury, U.K. The poison was thought to have been smeared on the door handle of their home but took effect later in Salisbury shopping centre. Both were extremely ill but survived after prolonged stays in hospital. Two other people were poisoned, one fatally, in nearby Amesbury when Charley Rowley found the discarded Novichok in a perfume bottle the following July. Dawn Sturgess, his partner, sprayed some on her wrists and Rowley got some on his hands which he then washed[82]. Both collapsed and were hospitalised but Sturgess died despite intensive treatment.

Novichok compounds are usually binary weapons and exactly what happened to both couples may never be known - clearly the material in the perfume bottle was a single chemical not two separate components. Unlike the earlier agents such as sarin, which break down in the environment, Novichok compounds are designed to be more persistent,[83] presenting a prolonged risk to health.

One puzzle, of many, relates to the timing. The Novichok which affected the Skripals was thought to have been smeared on their doorknob which they apparently handled on leaving the house. Nerve agents like this normally act within minutes but it was some time later that they collapsed on a bench in Salisbury shopping centre.

Nicotine

Nicotine is a clear, colourless liquid which goes yellow-brown on exposure to light. It is familiar as the addictive stimulant in tobacco and e-liquids but is not responsible for the yellow and brown staining on smokers' fingers or decorations in rooms where people smoke. Tobacco tars are the cause but most people refer to nicotine stains, although Stuart MacBride got this right in *A Dark So Deadly* (2017).

Formerly used as an insecticide, nicotine is a highly toxic alkaloid found in all parts of the tobacco plant, although the leaves contain the highest concentration. It is readily absorbed through the skin, lungs, mucous membranes of the mouth and nose, and the intestines. Depending on the dose, and the individual, it can take an hour for nicotine to be absorbed through the skin but inhaled nicotine can reach the brain in seven seconds[84].

Nicotine acts on the nervous system and at low doses it is a stimulant. The symptoms of dizziness, nausea, vomiting, headache, sweating and increased heart rate may be remembered by smokers from their first puffs of a cigarette. Higher doses may result in respiratory depression, slowing of the heart, convulsions, coma and death from respiratory paralysis[85]. The severe effects of swallowed nicotine may appear within an hour[86] but death can be rapid or take up to four hours[87].

The lethal dose of nicotine in humans has been a matter of some debate with some references giving a value of about 60mg. Others state that it is more than 500mg[88] but this will depend on the route of entry and the person's susceptibility. The lower figure is likely to apply to injected or inhaled nicotine while the

latter is relevant to the ingested chemical[89].
Tolerance to nicotine develops and it would take more to kill a seasoned smoker than someone who has never smoked or vaped.

There is no doubt that nicotine is a highly dangerous substance and numerous fatalities have occurred, often through its use as a pesticide. It has been used for murder (see case study) and a teenager in the U.S. used it to commit suicide[90].

In fiction Agatha Christie employed it in *Three Act Tragedy* (1935) and Ruth Rendell, in *Unacceptable Levels* (1995), had a woman poisoning her husband with nicotine patches - he was a smoker and the patches, which she substituted for plasters, augmented his nicotine intake to fatal levels.

Nicotine cannot be purchased as a pesticide anymore but it can be extracted from tobacco by boiling to make a "nicotine tea". This was advocated as a "green" insecticide in a number of environmental publications but its nicotine content is variable depending on the tobacco it is made from. As a murder weapon it would be unreliable, not least because it tastes dreadful. It is possible to extract purer nicotine from tobacco with a certain amount of chemical knowledge but there is no need for your character to do this when e-liquids are available in the High Street and online.

The amount of nicotine permitted in e-liquid supplies is controlled by law. The concentrate used to make up a vaping liquid must not contain more than 20mg of nicotine per ml and the maximum size of the refill is 10ml, giving a nicotine content of 200mg. Depending on which references are correct this is either about three fatal doses or two-fifths of a fatal dose. The flavoured and diluted vaping liquid, of course, will contain a smaller dose. E-cigarettes have been responsible for the deaths of children[91] and there has been a least one death from ingesting the stronger versions available in the US[92].

Case study: Lethal injection[93]

> It took twenty years for the authorities to convict Paul Curry, a Kansas nuclear engineer, of poisoning his wife. In 1994 Curry killed his wife with a nicotine injection after sedating her. According to prosecutors he had been slowly poisoning his wife during the previous year with another substance but finally killed her on the 9th of June. He called an ambulance once she was dead and although the police suspected him of murder the case went cold until new evidence about the timings around her death emerged in 2007. He was arrested in 2010 and convicted in November 2014, receiving a life sentence.

Opiates and opioids

The pain-relieving effects of opium, the resin produced by the Opium Poppy *Papaver somniferum*, have been known for millennia and the euphoric effects for probably just as long. Opium, which has been smoked to produce a blissful trance or dissolved in brandy to form the tincture laudanum, contains three main narcotic ingredients: morphine, codeine and thebaine. The first two have been used medically and all three are known as opiates since they come directly from opium.

Heroin (diamorphine) is derived from morphine via a simple chemical reaction and is also sometimes referred to as an opiate although some people classify it as an opioid.

Opioids are synthetic or semi-synthetic chemicals which resemble opiates biochemically and have the same general effects. They are powerful painkillers as well as sedatives and are sometimes used for anaesthesia. Like opiates, they are also highly addictive. Common opioids are hydrocodone (Vicodin), oxycodone (Percocet, OxyContin), pethidine, methadone and fentanyl.

Opiates and opioids are generally encountered in crime fiction as merchandise although many authors have portrayed characters with addiction problems and, sometimes, overdoses. In most countries these substances are tightly controlled and users inevitably come into contact with criminals - although there is an epidemic of over-prescribed opioids in the U.S. at the time of writing. The problem with street-bought drugs is the quality control. Street heroin is never pure diamorphine - it is always cut with other substances to increase the dealers' profits. Periodically, a batch of higher purity hits the streets and addicts accustomed to a lower quality accidentally overdose. Sometimes the additive used to cut the drug is particularly dangerous - there have been numerous deaths in the North of England from fentanyl added to heroin. It is some 100 times as toxic as diamorphine.

Fentanyl is used in patch form for pain relief because it is absorbed through the skin. In June 2018 the drug was linked to the death of a fifteen-month girl in Cornwall. It appeared that a fentanyl patch, used by the child's mother, transferred to her as they slept in the same bed[94].

If it is caught in time, opiate and opioid poisoning can be treated. An injection with naloxone will reverse the effects of the drugs and the patient can recover with appropriate treatment. Naloxone is carried routinely in ambulances and some British community drug abuse workers also carry it for use in an emergency.

Death caused by opiates and opioids is from respiratory depression - the patient can no longer breathe. Long term users build up a tolerance which reduces their effectiveness in both alleviating pain and inducing a high. While most deaths are accidental, these compounds have been used to murder people, most notably by Harold Shipman (see case study).

Agatha Christie used morphine in *Sad Cypress* (1940) and *By the Pricking of my Thumbs* (1968) while Lee Child presented a sensitive account of fentanyl addiction in a war veteran in *The Midnight Line* (2017).

The more powerful versions of these drugs are strictly controlled and would be difficult for your character to obtain without access to a pharmacy - and in some instances only a hospital pharmacy. Buying them on the street has its risks, not only from the product but also from the suppliers and the police.

Case study: The lethal GP[95]

Between 1978 and 1998 Dr Harold Shipman murdered a still-unknown number of patients with injections of diamorphine in the North of England. He preyed on elderly women whose deaths would not necessarily arouse suspicion. He also stole from his patients and forged the will of one woman, making himself the beneficiary, before he killed her. At these times there was no national system for spotting an unusual number of deaths in a GP practice so Shipman got away with it until suspicions were raised, by a taxi driver, a funeral director and another local doctor, about the frequency of deaths in his patients. Eventually he was arrested and charged with fifteen murders, appearing in court in October 1999. Following his conviction, and life sentences, an inquiry was set up headed by a High Court judge who concluded that Shipman had definitely murdered 215 people and identified an additional 45 highly suspicious deaths as well as 38 possible murders although the evidence was incomplete. In January 2004 Shipman killed himself in jail.

Palytoxin

Keeping tropical fish is not usually considered to be a dangerous activity but if your tank contains certain types of coral you are harbouring a deadly poison. Corals in the genus *Zoanthus* contain the chemical palytoxin, one of the most toxic substances known. It causes severe irritation to the skin if the corals are handled without protective gloves. If ingested or inhaled, as dust from dried material, it causes serious illness[96]. In March 2018 ten people were taken to hospital in Oxfordshire when the substance escaped following the cleaning of a fish tank. Four firefighters were affected while dealing with the leak[97]. So, if your plot features a murderous aquarist, poison is readily to hand.

Pesticides

While military nerve agents are clearly beyond the reach of your killer, some old pesticides which act in the same way may not be. The most toxic compounds have been banned in the U.K. for some time but old stocks may remain in farmers' sheds and stores. In 2011 a Scottish gamekeeper was fined £3,300 for possessing 10kg of carbofuran, an insecticide which acts in a similar way to the organophosphorus compounds above[98]. Banned in 2001, this highly toxic chemical has been used to kill birds of prey on and around shooting estates to protect the shooters' targets. It is quite possible that illegal stocks of this, and similar compounds, remain, either kept deliberately or simply forgotten about.

Insecticides have generally been the most toxic pesticides with herbicides (except for arsenic and a few other compounds) presenting less of a risk to humans. The main exception is paraquat, a powerful weedkiller now banned in the EU and many other countries. Approximately two and a half grams of the pure substance are likely to be lethal to most people[99]. There have been numerous deaths from this chemical, through accidental ingestion, suicide and murder. Although banned in most western countries paraquat is still used in the developing world where poisoning from it remains a "main medical problem"[100].

Paraquat can take days to kill. Initial symptoms of poisoning are sore throat, vomiting and shortness of breath. If a large dose is taken the patient may die within a day from metabolic acidosis and hyperglycaemia. With smaller lethal doses the lungs develop pulmonary fibrosis and fill up with fluid - a condition known as paraquat lung.

Death occurs from respiratory failure up to several days later[101]. There is no antidote once a lethal dose is absorbed but gastric lavage and supportive therapy can save life if provided very soon after the material is swallowed.

Murder by paraquat is not easy, at least in the U.K. Following a series of deaths, including those of children, the manufacturer put other chemicals into paraquat weedkillers to make them extremely bitter and hard to drink. The products available to gardeners, which could possibly still lurk in a garden shed, were much more dilute than the high-strength formulations restricted to professional farmers and growers. Nevertheless, people did sometimes steal the concentrated products from their employers so there may still be some, in sheds or barns, which your poisoner could use.

Real life paraquat murderers include the American serial poisoner Steven Catlin[102] and the Essex killer Susan Barber (see case study below). A notorious failed attempt, known as the poisoned pants case, involved a Chinese woman soaking her husband's underpants in paraquat and letting them dry, hoping that he would absorb a lethal dose through the skin. He suffered some intimate irritation which did not prove fatal[103].

Case study: Poison in Essex[104]

In 1981 Susan Barber was discovered in bed with her lover by Michael, her husband, so she decided to get rid of him. The means was easy - there was a bottle of Gramoxone (professional strength paraquat) in the shed and she added this to his gravy on more than one occasion, increasing the dose until it killed him. Michael Barber's death was listed as cardiac arrest, renal failure and pneumonia but the two pathologists who carried out the autopsy were suspicious and, thinking he may have been poisoned, preserved his organs in formalin for future reference. Subsequent analyses of these tissues revealed the presence of paraquat and in November 1982 Susan Barber and her lover appeared in court charged with murder. Despite Susan claiming that she only wanted to hurt Michael, both defendants eventually pleaded guilty. The case would have been proven considerably sooner had hospital staff sent blood and urine samples for testing, as instructed by the consultant, when Michael was hospitalised. They forgot to do so and covered up their error by claiming the results were negative. The results would not have helped Michael - he was already dying - but would have made justice swifter.

Phosgene

Phosgene is a poisonous gas used against troops in World War 1 and is also an important industrial chemical. It has not been used as murder weapon, unless you count warfare, but has caused fatalities in industry[105]. It is not available to the general public but I am including it here because it can be formed when a now-banned paint stripper, dichloromethane, comes into contact with a flame. Under the right circumstances this could prove lethal[106].

Potassium chloride

Potassium chloride is one of the ingredients of the lethal injections used to execute prisoners in some U.S. states. Its function is to stop the heart. A simple chemical, potassium chloride is an ingredient of the low-salt substitutes for sodium chloride - table salt. It has medical uses as well and this enabled the serial killer Orville Majors to murder his patients (see below). Potassium chloride is not a controlled substance and is easily obtainable. From your villain's point of view it is not an ideal weapon since it has to be injected - it's bitter taste would make it difficult to feed someone a lethal dose. Although potassium is present naturally in the body, greatly elevated levels would probably be detected and the injection site would attract suspicion. If the victim was already suffering from heart disease, doctors might not look too closely. Beverley Allitt (see above) used potassium chloride to kill some of her victims[107].

Case study: A killer nurse[108]

Orville Majors was a nurse, at a hospital in Indiana, who poisoned an unknown number of his patients. After he was appointed, the death rate in the hospital shot up with most of these deaths occurring while he was on duty. After two years the hospital became sufficiently suspicious to suspend Majors and exhume some of his former patients. In six cases, traces suggesting potassium chloride had been used were found. In December 1997, when Majors was arrested, vials of potassium chloride and syringes were found at his home. He was convicted of six murders but it was never established exactly how many people he had killed.

Ricin

Ricin is probably the most toxic chemical known to have been used as a murder weapon. It is a simple protein found in the seeds of the Castor Bean plant, *Ricinus communis*, and less than a milligram can be enough to kill an adult if injected under the skin[109]. When swallowed, ricin is partly broken down by digestive juices into harmless chemicals but even so it can be fatal - around 100mg is an estimated oral lethal dose.

Ricin kills by disrupting the mechanism in cells which make proteins, notably the enzymes which control cellular processes. Without these, cells die and organs fail. Symptoms take a few hours to appear and death occurs within three or four days as a rule. Someone poisoned by ricin but surviving for five days is likely to survive[110]. The symptoms of ricin poisoning can be difficult to identify as most doctors are unlikely to have encountered it before.

It is most unlikely that a patient presenting with ricin poisoning would be tested for the substance, especially as a highly sophisticated laboratory would be needed to carry out the test. Once major effects from a lethal dose begin to appear treatment is unlikely to be successful and palliative care is the only option

Exposure to very small amounts of ricin can stimulate the production of antibodies by the immune system, providing some protection against a later, larger, dose, and vaccines have been developed to protect troops who may be exposed to ricin in battle. Ricin is not widely available and laboratories using more than trace amounts must be registered.

The Castor Bean plant is common and is often seen in public parks. Only the seeds contain ricin and swallowing them is relatively safe (although not recommended) since the hard outer coating prevents the ricin from seeping out. Ricin can be extracted from the beans but doing so would be dangerous to an untrained operator and is also illegal under anti-terrorism legislation in the U.K. Agatha Christie used ricin in *The House of Lurking Death* (1929) and in real life the most notorious use of the poison for nefarious purposes was the assassination of Georgi Markov (see below).

Case study: Pellets of poison[111]

Georgi Markov was an exiled Bulgarian journalist whose broadcasts on Radio Free Europe were a source of irritation to the Bulgarian government. On the 7th September 1978 he was waiting for a bus and felt a sharp pain in his leg. On turning around he saw a man pick up a dropped umbrella and hasten away. That evening he began to feel ill and the following day he was taken to hospital where, four days later, he died. At autopsy, the pathologist found a tiny metal pellet, embedded in Markov's leg, and this was sent to Porton Down for analysis along with tissue samples. The pellet was found to have small holes drilled in it, enough to hold a lethal dose of ricin. Although ricin was not found in the pellet, it was provisionally identified by a process of elimination - virtually nothing else was that lethal. Originally it was thought that the pellet had been fired into Markov's leg by the umbrella but a more likely weapon was a concealed gas pistol[112].

Material suspected of being ricin was posted to President Trump at the Pentagon in 2018 but the facts here are unclear[113]

Strychnine

Strychnine is a highly toxic alkaloid which was once used medicinally as a "tonic" and also as a pesticide. Of the "traditional" poisons used by crime writers, strychnine is the nastiest since it causes an extremely painful death.

Strychnine oversensitises the nervous system so that the slightest stimulation will trigger a nerve impulse, contracting muscles with considerable force. A diagnostic feature is a powerful contraction of the muscles in the back which causes the body to arch convulsively - in extreme cases with just the head and heels resting on the ground. A characteristic fixed grin is also produced[114]. There are periods of relative calm between bouts of convulsions but death usually occurs within an hour, sometimes two[115], as the muscles controlling breathing are affected, leading to asphyxiation. Around 70mg of strychnine are likely to be lethal but some people may succumb to less[116].

Agatha Christie used strychnine in several stories, notably her first novel *The Mysterious Affair at Styles* (1921). She elegantly demonstrated her knowledge of pharmacology in this book which featured a cunning murder method. Conan Doyle also used it in *The Sign of Four* (1890).

In real life, strychnine has been used historically in a number of murders, notably by the Victorian serial poisoner Thomas Neill Cream[117]. It is far more difficult to get hold of in the U.K. than hitherto though, surprisingly, seeds containing the poison can be bought online. It is more widely available in other countries, however, and in 2015 David Lytton committed suicide on Saddleworth Moor using strychnine which he had brought with him from Pakistan[118].

Tetrodotoxin

The puffer fish (fugu) is a Japanese delicacy but it harbours a deadly poison. Correctly prepared it is perfectly safe to eat but if the chef accidentally includes the wrong parts of the fish in the meal it can kill, accounting for some 50 deaths in Japan per year during the 1990s[119]. The toxic ingredient is tetrodotoxin, a powerful nerve poison, 1-4 mg of which is estimated to be lethal[120]. Fugu is not widely available outside Japan but it may be imported into other countries.

In 2014 two people in Minnesota were hospitalised with tetrodotoxin poisoning after eating imported fugu but survived after supportive treatment[121].

Tetrodotoxin has been used in fiction - in Ian Fleming's *From Russia With Love* (1957) James Bond is stabbed and nearly killed by a blade coated with tetrodotoxin, the results of which are described at the beginning of *Dr No* (1958).

Tetrodotoxin is also found in other animals, notably some American newts which secrete it from their skin. This proved fatal for a man in Oregon who swallowed a Rough-skinned Newt (*Taricha granulosa*) after drinking heavily. He died later that day[122].
Getting hold of tetrodotoxin would be difficult for your killer as it is not on general sale. It has medical and research uses so

some suppliers may stock it. In 2012 a man from the Chicago area was sentenced to more than seven years in jail for obtaining enough tetrodotoxin to kill more than 20 people from a scientific supplier. He posed as a doctor and it was alleged he intended to use it to kill his wife[123]. Obtaining the animals which produce tetrodotoxin would also be difficult although there may be channels through which puffer fish can be imported illegally.

Thallium

Thallium is a highly poisonous metal which, biochemically, resembles potassium. This means it can substitute for potassium in numerous cellular processes, bringing them to a halt. It also disrupts the workings of vital enzymes by binding to their molecules.

A large single dose can prove fatal but thallium is also a cumulative poison with repeated smaller doses building up to a lethal level. Chronic symptoms include loss of hair, vomiting, stomach pains, generalised pain and hallucinations[124] (see the case study on p21 for an account of the most notorious thallium poisoner, Graham Young).

Robert Curley, an electrician in Pennsylvania, was fatally poisoned by his wife, Joann, using rat poison containing thallium. By monitoring the levels of thallium in his hair, nails and other tissues, investigators were able to show that only Joann was present every time a peak occurred[125]. In August 1991 Curley was hospitalised with flu-like symptoms, numbness and pains in his hands and feet. He also began vomiting and losing his hair. Once in hospital he started to improve and was discharged. Nine days later his condition deteriorated and he was readmitted. Some improvements followed and he was able to receive visitors, including his wife Joann, on the 22nd September but that night he became much worse and continued to decline. Five days later his wife agreed to the withdrawal of life support and he died.

The hospital had discovered high levels of thallium in Curley's system which could only have come through eating or drinking the poison. Exactly how this had happened was not clear and the death was classified as homicide. In 1994, however, a forensic toxicologist offered to investigate the timeline of Curley's thallium exposure and the body was exhumed. By analysing samples of hair and fingernails he showed that from late 1990 onwards the exposure had risen and fallen, culminating in the fatal dose in September 1991. Crucially, the final dose could only have been received when his family visited.

Further analysis showed that the only person having access to Curley when the other peaks of exposure occurred was his wife, who collected nearly $300,000 in insurance when he died. In July 1997 Joann Curley admitted murdering her husband for the insurance money and was sentenced to 20 years in prison[12]

Thallium is no longer available as a pesticide in the U.K. It is a regulated substance and anyone wishing to purchase thallium compounds for its remaining industrial or scientific uses needs a licence.

It is still available in other countries – in March 2019 a San Diego man received three life sentences for attempting to kill his wife with thallium over a period of several months[126].

Writing poisons (2)

- Theoretically there is a plethora of poisons available to a would-be killer and many have been tried, in fiction and in real life.
- Before choosing one for your killer, check how easy it is to obtain the substance.
- Check the signs and symptoms of poisoning by the chemical of choice to avoid common mistakes.
- Check how long it takes for symptoms to occur and which route of administration works.
- Check for possible treatments and antidotes.
- Ensure your killer takes precautions to avoid self-poisoning.

- Some materials are only available to a state or highly organised terrorist group.
- If in doubt about a substance, look it up or ask someone.

CHAPTER 3: PRODUCING UNCONSCIOUSNESS

The basics

Knocking someone out by various means is a staple plot device. Unfortunately, there is much received "unwisdom" about how chemicals, particularly chloroform, can be used to produce unconsciousness. Knocking your characters out is not as simple as it seems and many novels, TV series and films play fast and loose with pharmacology, biochemistry and human anatomy. This does not mean it's impossible, as the case studies and examples below will show. In this chapter we will see how the anaesthetic drugs favoured by writers work, the pitfalls to avoid, and will also look at other means of temporarily sending your victim to sleep.

Chemical methods

Before choosing a knockout drug you need to find answers to a number of questions:

- How will it get into the victim's system?;
- How quickly does it act?;
- How long does it last?;
- Are there side effects? and
- How will your character get hold of it?

With the answers to these questions to hand you can begin to write a credible scenario.

Anaesthetics work by modifying the workings of the brain and spinal cord so, clearly, they must reach these organs before anything happens. This takes time. When a drug is injected into a vein the bloodstream carries it swiftly to the brain and it will work within seconds. Injected into a muscle, however, it will take longer as the drug has to diffuse through the tissues into blood vessels which then carry it to the brain. This can take a number of minutes.

A common plot device, whereby a quick stab with a syringe causes instant unconsciousness, is just not feasible as the chances of hitting a vein during a surreptitious assault are minimal. Injecting enough of the drug would take several seconds and cause pain so the victim would be able to escape, fight back or call for help before any effects were felt. Of course, if the victim is already passive as a result of a previous dose, or a physical injury, it's much easier to find a vein.

Inhalation anaesthetics are also quick to work, when used for surgery, as the gas or vapour is readily absorbed through the lungs and into the bloodstream. They are quicker to act than drugs taken orally. A key issue with these chemicals is the need to maintain exposure. During an operation the anaesthetist will supply the drug continuously, monitoring its effects and adjusting the mixture of anaesthetic and oxygen appropriately. If the mixture is wrong the patient could die, suffer permanent brain damage, or come round too soon. Once the supply of anaesthetic is stopped, the patient will start to wake up.

Drugs taken orally are generally slowest to work. Some are absorbed through the lining of the mouth or stomach but once swallowed the chemical normally has to pass through the stomach, into the intestines for absorption, and then be conveyed by the blood to the part of the body it affects. This can take 15-20 minutes depending on what's in the stomach already and whether the drug is added to food or drink. Whether it's the traditional "*Mickey Finn*" or Rohypnol, the scenario whereby someone takes a sip of their drink and keels over ten seconds later is quite unfeasible.

So, let's look at some of the chemicals used, in real life and in fiction, to knock people out.

Chloroform

Chloroform is probably the most misunderstood chemical in crime fiction. It was one of the first general anaesthetics, famously used by Queen Victoria during childbirth. Prior to its introduction, some surgeons had employed nitrous oxide (laughing gas) and ether was also in use. Ether is an irritant to the lungs and sometimes caused coughing so when the sweeter-smelling and less unpleasant chloroform came along it rapidly supplanted ether. In fiction, chloroform is usually encountered soaked on a rag and pressed over the victim's mouth whereupon he or she lapses into unconsciousness for a considerable period of time. This is unrealistic on several counts. It takes at least five minutes of inhalation to produce unconsciousness during surgical anaesthesia with chloroform and inhalation has to be maintained if the victim is to remain asleep[1]. A safe mixture of air and vapour must be maintained. If someone is breathing nothing but chloroform they may pass out in less than five minutes but this will certainly not happen instantaneously. Prolonged inhalation of nothing but chloroform would be fatal.

A shorter exposure to chloroform can cause confusion and dizziness. Indeed, chloroform parties where people inhaled the vapour to become euphoric, or even drank small amounts in carbonated water resembling champagne, were popular in the mid-18th century[2]. Temporary disorientation from inhaled chloroform may be sufficiently enfeebling to enable a villain to rob or overpower someone by other means but the risk of this has been exaggerated. In Victorian times there were occasional claims that chloroform had been used in robberies but closer examination of the evidence showed these to be fanciful and the role of chloroform in a number of more recent cases is, at best, debatable[3].

In 1851 the eminent doctor John Snow, in a letter to the Lord Chief Justice, explained forcefully that it was impossible to chloroform someone against their will without using considerable violence[4] and this remains the case.

Case study: The chloroforming lab tech.[5]

In July 2010 Jared Shreeve, a laboratory technician, was convicted of administering chloroform to a pupil at the school in Ilford, Essex, where he worked. He soaked a mask in the substance and persuaded her to put it on, claiming it was to protect her against fumes from spilt chemicals. She became nauseous and dizzy and tried to remove the mask but Shreeve insisted that she wore it, adding more chloroform. Eventually she passed out and a teacher discovered Shreeve fanning her with a book. The pupil vomited, had a slight burn to the skin around her mouth from the chloroform and was taken to hospital.

Chloroform is poisonous if swallowed in any quantity but it has a strong and distinctive taste which would be difficult to disguise - even in a spirit such as whisky. In a pure state, or concentrated solution (e.g. in alcohol), it is an irritant and would cause a burning sensation if swallowed. Applied to delicate skin, it can cause minor burn-like lesions.

In one published crime novel it was suggested that a man may have been killed by injected chloroform, although how the killer would have been able to hold down a fit adult male while administering an injection was not explained. The irritant effect on the delicate lining of the victim's veins would have been agonising. The same author stated that chloroform had been used to keep a rabbit unconscious while an artist sculpted it - specialist equipment would have been needed to maintain exposure and the rabbit would probably have died.

At room temperature, chloroform is highly volatile and evaporates quickly. Unless it is used in an unventilated room, traces will disappear fairly rapidly. A detective arriving on the scene shortly afterwards might be able to smell its sweetish odour but after a few hours in a normal home it would probably be gone unless soaked material was left at the scene. Highly specialised equipment might be able to detect traces in forensic samples collected at the scene but this type of kit may not be readily available. The substance can be detected in the body after death in blood, the brain, the liver, the kidneys and, particularly, in fatty tissues[6].

Chloroform has been used as a murder weapon, notably in the case of Adelaide Bartlett who was acquitted of poisoning her husband in 1886 although it is more than probable that she was guilty. This case, and a number of others where chloroform was involved, is ably described in Linda Stratmann's excellent book *Chloroform - the quest for oblivion*[7].

Chloroform is no longer used in anaesthesia because the difference between an anaesthetic dose and a harmful dose is too small - it had the unfortunate property of stopping the heart in too many patients. Chloroform water - a dilute solution - has been used as a preservative in medicines but this was discontinued some years ago owing to chloroform's toxicity. It is a restricted substance and is not available to the general public, although there are some industrial and laboratory uses.

Ether, which, like chloroform, used to be on sale to the public for removing grease stains from clothes, has been used in robberies. Ex-Detective Superintendent Robert Fabian, in his memoirs *Fabian of the Yard*, recounts how a thief used an ether-soaked handkerchief to overpower women whom he then robbed, although his account confuses ether with chloroform in places[8].

Chloral hydrate

Chemically similar to chloroform, chloral hydrate is a liquid sedative and hypnotic which is rarely used in medicine these days. Added to alcoholic drinks it was the original "*Mickey Finn*", named after a Chicago bartender who used to knock out his customers with the chemical, in the early 1900s, prior to stealing their money[9]. As with many anaesthetics it is difficult to get the dose right and there is a risk of serious poisoning. Other drugs (see below) have superseded chloral hydrate for nefarious purposes but a story set in the 1950s or earlier could credibly feature this chemical.

Midazolam

Midazolam crops up in crime fiction as a knock-out agent but, unfortunately, writers - and screenwriters - often make mistakes when using it. Midazolam is used as a general anaesthetic, although usually in combination with other drugs, and is normally given intravenously. In order to prevent heart problems it is injected slowly, over a period of 20-30 seconds. Sedation starts in a couple of minutes and its full effects appear after three to five minutes[10]. The scenario where someone feels a prick in the back of the neck, or is stabbed with a syringe, and instantly falls asleep simply would not work. Finding a vein in someone's neck, e.g. when they're sitting in front of you in a pub, would be impossible and they would certainly notice your efforts. Injecting midazolam into a muscle, in the neck or elsewhere, causes significant pain and sedation takes around 15 minutes to appear by this route, with the peak effects only developing after 30-60 minutes[11].

Midazolam is a short duration anaesthetic and recovery, which includes standing and walking around, takes two to six hours[12]. Consciousness returns much sooner than that so the scene where someone remains asleep for hours after one dose is unrealistic, although some individuals are particularly susceptible and take longer to recover. The drug is rapidly removed from the body and would be difficult to detect after 48 hours. A valuable property of midazolam is its production of amnesia - patients well sedated with it do not remember unpleasant procedures such as colonoscopies and some types of dentistry.

Midazolam is also used as an oral sedative, with peak effects occurring in about 30 minutes[13]. Someone taking a sedative dose would be drowsy and uncoordinated and a larger dose could produce unconsciousness. Getting someone to take a large dose orally could be difficult as midazolam is bitter to the taste - when given to children prior to minor surgery it is often mixed with orange juice.

In some countries (not the U.K.) patients experiencing prolonged epileptic seizures may be given midazolam in a nasal spray while a combination of midazolam and a local anaesthetic is sometimes sprayed into the noses of patients by dentists to sedate them before surgery. These formulations could possibly be used by your protagonist to sedate someone - midazolam acts quickly by this route - but it would be difficult to hold someone's head still enough to administer enough of the spray if they weren't co-operating.

In the U.K., prolonged seizures may be controlled by administering a solution of midazolam under the tongue (buccal) using a (needle-less) syringe. Someone already unconscious could be "topped up" by this route and it may be easier to steal this product from a source in the community rather than to acquire the intravenous solution from a hospital.

Case study: Rape and manslaughter[14]

> In May 2000 Kevin Cobb, a nurse, was convicted, in the U.K., of the manslaughter of a female colleague and of drugging and raping three female patients under his care. His colleague, Susan Annis, died after Cobb spiked her cider with midazolam in order to rape her. Normally the dose he used would not kill but in combination with alcohol it proved fatal. Although traces of midazolam were discovered in Annis's stomach at the post mortem, they were dismissed as irrelevant. It was only when Cobb's last victim woke during the rape that he was arrested, after which two other women came forward. This prompted a re-investigation of Annis's death when a colleague contacted the police. Police now suspect that Cobb may have raped many more women who did not realise what had happened because of midazolam's amnesia-producing property. Following the Cobb case, controls on midazolam were tightened in 2008.

Ketamine

Ketamine, known as "Special K" among other street names, is a short-acting anaesthetic used in hospitals and by vets. It is a dissociative anaesthetic which means that patients feel detached from reality and don't notice pain. Because of the detachment and hallucinations which it produces, ketamine is used recreationally - sometimes with unpleasant side effects. C.J. Carver's *Spare Me the Truth* (2016) includes a vivid description of the effects of ketamine.

When ketamine is injected into a vein, unconsciousness can occur in around 30 seconds and lasts for five to ten minutes[15]. Injections into a muscle take longer (three to four minutes) to produce effects, lasting for 12-25 minutes, as the drug is released into the system more slowly[16]. When ketamine is swallowed, dissociative effects occur between five and twenty minutes later[17], the intensity depending on the dose and the individual. Whether used medically or recreationally, ketamine can produce some unpleasant psychological side effects which may persist for some time. Peter James used ketamine, injected into an already concussed cyclist, to maintain unconsciousness in *You Are Dead* (2015).

Ketamine disappears from the body quickly which is why it can be difficult to prove it's been used in cases of date-rape (see below). A spot test for ketamine in urine can detect residues up to two days after the chemical has been taken as a single dose, provided that a significant quantity is involved[18].
More sophisticated analyses would be needed to detect smaller doses or those taken a longer time previously.

Other anaesthetics
The gases and volatile liquids used as general anaesthetics in hospitals are not really suitable for nefarious purposes since specialist equipment is needed to apply them and exposure has to be continuous to maintain unconsciousness. There are other, intravenous, anaesthetics which could work, however. Propofol is a short-acting drug which can cause unconsciousness within 30 seconds when injected correctly[19] although it is generally injected at a slower rate prior to surgery. Synthetic opioids such as fentanyl can also be used although these are extremely powerful and, like most anaesthetic drugs, can cause death if too much is administered.

Immobilon (etorphine plus a sedative) is the drug used in tranquilliser darts to knock out elephants, rhinos and other large mammals in game parks. It has been used in general veterinary practice in the past but has been discontinued owing to its extreme toxicity. The dose estimated to be fatal to half the individuals in the human population (LD50) is quoted as thirty millionths of a gram[20]. It is always supplied with enough antidote. which must be given immediately in case of accidental injection, to reverse Immobilon's effects.

Tranquilliser darts are not used on humans, despite their popularity in books and TV programmes from *The Man From U.N.C.L.E.*[a] onwards. A fixed dose would not affect some people and would be potentially lethal for others (see Chapter 1). Even if the dose was correct, the time taken for it to work would give the target plenty of opportunity to continue fighting or escape. Tasers and other electric stun guns are the (usually) non-lethal immobilisation devices used by police forces - and, increasingly, by criminals in fiction.

Case study: Vet in the frame[21]

> In 1995, vet Ryan James was convicted of killing his wife by spiking her orange juice with Immobilon. It wasn't until the discovery of his wife's suicide note that he was able to appeal successfully against his conviction, having spent three and a half years in jail. His wife had hidden the note before killing herself, in order to frame him.

It is important to remember, when knocking people out with drugs, that overdoses can be fatal. Anaesthetists are highly skilled at ensuring their patients continue to breathe and their hearts still beat during surgery. This may not matter to some criminals but a dead victim may not be what they are looking for, at least at first. Also, residual effects such as confusion, drowsiness and poor co-ordination may persist after the victim wakes up. Coherent thought, combat or fast car chases are pretty much out of the question for some time.

Anaesthetic drugs are tightly controlled so would normally have to be stolen from a hospital or vet's surgery - high street pharmacists would be unlikely to stock most of them. Fentanyl has become available on the streets for opiate addicts and numerous fatalities have occurred when it has been added to heroin - 160 deaths were reported in the eighteen months leading up to December 2018[22]. Street fentanyl would not be suitable for your villain's purposes since its quality is poor and it may be contaminated with carfentanyl, an even more toxic substance. Some dealers on the dark web are reported to have stopped supplying it as the drug is attracting too much police attention[23].

Date rape drugs
Spiking someone's drink so that they can be incapacitated and raped or kidnapped is an all-too-common crime and several drugs are used by attackers. They generally have the advantage - to the attacker - that the victim has no memory of what has happened. They disappear from the body rapidly so obtaining evidence for a conviction can be difficult. Ketamine and midazolam have already been described, although midazolam is difficult to get hold of. Other date-rape drugs are available on the streets.

Rohypnol, or roofies, (flunitrazepam) is the best-known date rape drug. Added to a drink it produces confusion, sleepiness, unconsciousness and amnesia. Someone affected could be carried out of a club or pub, on the pretext that they were drunk, without anyone challenging the kidnapper.

Traces of flunitrazepam are eliminated from the body fairly quickly but its metabolite can be detected up to 21 days later if the correct technique is used[24] - although routine analyses would not be this sensitive. If the victim is killed shortly after absorbing the drug, the metabolite would be found after a few hours rather than the drug itself.

Temazepam, a sleeping pill which has often been misused on the streets by people seeking a high, was used, along with an antihistamine, in the Sharon Matthews case. Conspiring with her boyfriend's uncle, a woman kidnapped, sedated and kept hidden her own nine year old daughter, in a plot to claim the reward money posted for her return[25].

Flunitrazepam, midazolam and temazepam, along with the more familiar diazepam (Valium), are members of a group of drugs called benzodiazepines. They all have sedative effects, but their precise properties vary, and are only available on prescription. Some are controlled drugs. I have heard pathologists in TV programmes say "She had benzodiazepine in her system" as if there was only one type. This is incorrect: the individual drug would be named. Like most date-rape drugs, benzodiazepines are more potent when combined with alcohol. Diazepam can be highly addictive and internet purchasing of diazepam is an issue of current concern, not least because some of the tablets bought in this way have proved to be lethal fakes[27].

Case study: The black cab rapist[26]

In March 2009 John Worboys, a London taxi driver, was convicted of 19 charges involving drugging, assaulting and, in one case, raping women who had got into his cab. He would claim that he had won in the lottery or at a casino and invite them to celebrate with a glass of champagne. The drink contained temazepam and, once they were unconscious, he would attack them. He had been doing this for at least six years before he was arrested for the rape of a lawyer, at which point the police began to link other cases. The publicity around the trial and subsequent review led to many more incidents being reported to the police, who believed that over 100 passengers could have been drugged and assaulted during his 13 years of taxi driving in London and Dorset. In May 2019 further charges were brought against Warboys, now known as John Radford.

GHB - gamma-hydroxybutyrate - is a recreational drug known as (among other things) G or Gina, popular on the club scene. It is produced in small quantities in the body, and is present in red wine, but much larger amounts are used by clubbers to produce feelings of relaxation, euphoria and increased libido. It takes effect in 15-30 minutes and lasts for three to six hours[28]. Higher doses can cause dizziness and confusion, nausea and vomiting, unconsciousness and, in extreme cases, coma and death[29]. Added to a drink as a liquid, it is not easy to taste and in combination with alcohol rapidly produces disorientation, unconsciousness and amnesia. It has been used frequently as a date-rape drug, with men being the victims in 10-15% of such crimes (2003 figures)[30].

GHB was controlled under the U.K. Misuse of Drugs Act 1971 in 2003 but two similar substances, gamma-butyrolactone (GBL), and 1,4-butanediol, were not so classified until 2009. GBL is marketed as a paint stripper for cleaning off graffiti and has been implicated in a number of deaths[31]. It is converted to

GHB in the body, a conversion which can also be achieved easily at home with a simple chemical reaction.
Personal accounts of GHB use, and its addictive properties, are included in a Guardian article published in November 2018[32].

GHB is eliminated from the body very quickly. It is detectable in blood and saliva for up to five hours and in urine for less than twelve[33]. Detecting GHB residues is complicated by the natural levels in the body, so a correction must be made for amounts present before any of the drug is taken. Post mortem samples can give misleading results since storage conditions can affect levels in samples and in some tissues levels can actually rise after death.

Case study: Rape and murder[34]

In 2016 Stephen Port, a Londoner, was sentenced to life imprisonment for the murder of four men he met via gay social media sites. He invited them back to his flat, plied them with drinks spiked with GHB and raped them. Although he may not have intended to kill, the high levels of GHB involved proved fatal, hence the murder conviction. The police investigation into the murders was found to be flawed and the Metropolitan Police subsequently launched a review of 58 other deaths connected with GHB.

Hyoscine, also known as scopolamine, has also been used to incapacitate people - it can make people easily controllable and there have been cases where drugged victims have been robbed or compelled to withdraw money from cash machines[35]. It was also reported to have been used in 1910 as a murder weapon in London, U.K., by Dr Crippen[36].

Spice

Synthetic cannabinoids are chemicals similar to the active ingredients of cannabis. Collectively known as spice, these could be used to disorientate someone sufficiently to kidnap them. They are not anaesthetics but produce incapacitating symptoms which make the victim appear drunk - spice is known as the zombie drug because of its dramatic effects. It is cheap but can be extremely dangerous as heart attacks and psychotic episodes are reported side effects. Spice is a major problem in prisons where it has been linked with outbreaks of violence and severe mental health problems. Used recreationally, the material is usually dissolved in solvents and sprayed onto plant material, such as tobacco, which is then smoked. Your character could spray it onto a normal cigarette or mix the powder into food in order to overpower a victim.

Psychedelics
Disorientation, although not unconsciousness, is caused by a wide range of psychedelic drugs such as LSD, mescaline and psilocybin (in magic mushrooms). These could be used by a character to control someone although the odd behaviour which sometimes occurs could be a problem. Chris Simms used LSD to disorient someone in the short story *High Flyer* (2017) but to say more would spoil the plot.

Over the counter
Many common drugs, including over-the-counter medicines, can produce drowsiness. Antihistamine tablets, such as meclozine, cinnarizine and promethazine, are given to prevent travel sickness or help with allergies and are sometimes used as mild sedatives. They are unlikely to knock someone out, unless given in excessively large doses, but can produce sleepiness, especially if combined with alcohol. Some cough mixtures also contain ingredients which can make you drowsy although not, generally, unconscious. Getting someone to ingest a sufficiently large quantity of these drugs could be a challenge.

Asphyxiants
It is worth mentioning that unconsciousness can be induced by inert gases which simply deprive the brain of oxygen. Nitrogen, carbon dioxide and fire extinguishing gases can all do this but this is not a reliable way of knocking someone out as they tend to die if oxygen is not supplied promptly. In some slaughterhouses, animals are immersed in carbon dioxide before being killed. This does not anaesthetise them but makes them less agitated.
Carbon monoxide (see Chapter 2) will also cause sleepiness and unconsciousness although this is not strictly asphyxia. It is often fatal and not recommended for producing reversible

unconsciousness.

Case study: Christie and carbon monoxide[37]

John Christie was a serial killer and rapist active in Notting Hill Gate, London, U.K., during the 1940s and 1950s. He used town gas, which contained 15% carbon monoxide, to make four of his victims drowsy, after which he raped and strangled them. In one case he persuaded a woman that inhaling a "special mixture", comprising decongestant vapours to which he added the gas, would cure her bronchitis. He killed at least eight people and was hanged in 1953.

In fiction, M.J. Arlidge's killer used carbon monoxide from a vehicle exhaust to subdue campers in *Down to the Woods* (2018) - some had been drinking so did not smell the exhaust or hear the engine, presumably.

Mass anaesthesia

A popular device in films and books is the anaesthetic gas pumped into a room or vehicle which causes the occupants to fall asleep within a few seconds. Unfortunately, this is largely fantasy and an attempt to do this in real life proved tragic, as described in the "*Death at the Theatre*" case study below.

A type of question which has been used in pharmacy degree examinations is "What substance would you use to immobilise a gang of hijackers holding hostages in an aircraft?"

The question tests the students' understanding of several important principles:

- People respond differently to the same dose of a drug (see Chapter 1) hence some people would be seriously affected, possibly fatally, while others would be only mildly influenced.

- Some passengers may have health conditions, such as heart disease, which could make them particularly sensitive to the drug and which could prove fatal.

- It would be impossible to distribute the anaesthetic agent evenly through the aircraft's ventilation system (which might be shut down anyway) so the doses received would be wildly variable.

- Finally, assuming a sufficient dose was received by each of the hijackers, it would take some time before they became unconscious and they would certainly realise what was happening - even if the smell of the anaesthetic didn't give the game away. They would have plenty of time to shoot the hostages or detonate the bomb before passing out.
  In short, it wouldn't work.

Case study: Death at the theatre[38]

In 2002, 40-50 armed Chechen separatists occupied Moscow's Dubrovka theatre, taking 850 hostages and planting explosive charges around the building. The structure of the theatre meant that a conventional military attack would have been extremely difficult so special forces from the F.S.B. pumped an incapacitating agent, in the form of an aerosol, into the building's ventilation system, hoping to subdue the terrorists. Unfortunately, up to 204 hostages died from the effects of the aerosol. All the terrorists were reported killed, either by the drug or by gunfire. The Russians didn't identify the agent concerned at the time but later admitted that it was based on fentanyl[39].

In 2015 it was suggested that the racing driver, Jenson Button, and his wife had been anaesthetised while they slept, with a gas pumped into their St Tropez villa's air conditioning system by robbers. Rumours of several similar incidents were circulating in parts of France and Spain where "gassing gangs" were supposed to be active. The Royal College of Anaesthetists, however, dismissed these reports as a myth and its Vice-President, Dr Liam Brennan, was at pains to point out to journalists why such a ploy would not work[40].

A favourite device in some older thrillers (including stories by Leslie Charteris, author of the Saint titles) is the taxi which

has anaesthetic gas pumped into the passenger compartment, knocking out its occupants within a few seconds. Apart from the problems of making the back of the vehicle gas-tight, there is no gas which would work that quickly. Anyone reasonably quick-witted would realise what was happening and kick a window out - laminated glass was not around in the thirties.
If someone was unable to escape and was knocked out by an inhalation anaesthetic (a mixture of nitrous oxide and isoflurane pumped into the back of a van was used in a recent thriller), maintaining unconsciousness for a prolonged period without killing the subject would require the services of a trained anaesthetist.

Sources of supply
Most of the chemicals described in this chapter are difficult to obtain. They are usually controlled drugs or prescription-only medicines. Some may be held only by hospitals rather than local pharmacists. In the case of chloroform there is no remaining medical use for it and it cannot be bought over the counter in the U.K., although a recognised laboratory or business having a legitimate need for it can purchase it from specialist suppliers.

Some substances can be bought from other countries via the internet. It is not illegal to import some medicines but doing so will inevitably leave a trail. Importing controlled drugs - which includes some benzodiazepines - is an offence although it seems to be a widespread practice as patients refused these medicines by their GPs seek other sources of supply. Buying drugs on the street is risky for several reasons - the police may be watching the dealer, the dealer could rob your character and the quality of the product would be suspect. There is, of course, the dark web with its suppliers who are prepared to dispatch items disguised as legitimate goods, in an attempt to slip them through customs. Serious criminals (and skilled teenagers) will know how to use it. Ordinary people probably won't - and, anyway, isn't it a bit of a plot cop-out?

Non-chemical methods
Hitting someone over the head is a time-honoured means of knocking someone out in fiction - but how realistic is it?

The answer is that it depends much on the strength of the blow, where it is struck and the susceptibility of the victim. The consequences, too, are variable.

A blow to the head, be it a punch, a strike with a solid item or a fall, can cause concussion involving temporary unconsciousness (a few seconds to a few minutes)[41]. Here the brain is simply shaken up and there may be no permanent damage, apart from the victim forgetting what happened. The victim is likely to feel sick while confusion and wooziness may last for some time.

A more serious situation arises when blood vessels within the skull rupture. The brain is surrounded by membranes (meninges) and if blood collects between them (a subdural haematoma) or between the skull and the outer membrane (an epidural, or extradural, haematoma) pressure builds up on the brain. In both cases there is a loss of consciousness and this may progress fatally[42]. In the latter case the victim may recover after a few minutes and remain conscious but deteriorate later unless treated[43]. The time between injury and death from a head injury is highly variable.

Any head injury involving a loss of consciousness requires urgent medical attention and someone knocked out in this way is not going to leap up ten minutes later and re-enter the fray - if they are unconscious for more than a few minutes they may well have suffered permanent brain damage[44]. There have been cases reported in the press in recent years where a single punch has proved fatal although the assailants did not intend to kill (see Chapter 7).

A sideways blow to the jaw causes the head to spin around, especially if the victim's neck muscles are not tensed beforehand. As the head spins the brain, which is floating in fluid, lags behind and hits the inside of the skull causing shock and unconsciousness. Another possible consequence, particularly if the attacker is not wearing boxing gloves, is a broken jaw. Sharon Bolton's *Daisy in Chains* (2016) describes a fight where an imprisoned doctor uses his knowledge of anatomy to subdue his attackers.

Repeated blows to the head will eventually cause permanent damage such as loss of coordination, diminished intellectual function and dementia. This is well known in boxers who have been repeatedly knocked out or just hit on the head frequently but it is also seen in other sports such as American football.

The situation is summed up neatly on Quora by Tommy Thompson, an Electroneurodiagnostic Technician in the US:[45]

> *"There is no safe way to be knocked out. TV and films are not sending an accurate message when you see your hero knocked out repeatedly episode after episode. This guy's brain would be mush long before the season ended. By the season finale he would be wearing a helmet and mittens and talking gibberish."*

Another possible consequence of being struck on the head is a skull fracture. This could be a simple crack in one of the bones, which will heal itself in time, or could be more serious. A depressed skull fracture is where broken bone is forced inwards, pressing on the brain and meninges, possibly causing a haematoma and death. This requires surgery and there may be lasting effects. Although the skull is tough, implements which strike it are often tougher - if you are hit over the head with a bottle, the bottle is unlikely to break but your skull might (see Chapter 7). The skull is not uniformly strong - some areas are more susceptible to breakage than others. The bone around the eye sockets, the temples, various elements of the base of the skull and the parietal bones (which form the sides and top of the skull) are among the weakest parts.

Another staple of TV and films is the knock out karate chop to the neck, more properly known as a knife hand strike.
It doesn't work on the back of the neck - spinal damage could result - but when applied to the side of the neck by a skilled practitioner it can be effective. Apart from the pain, which can temporarily disorientate, the impact on the carotid artery can briefly stop the flow of blood to the brain, causing unconsciousness. Also, hitting the area around the vagus nerve, which runs from the brain down the neck to the rest of the body, can cause disorientation, dizziness and temporary unconscious-

ness[46]. This technique is not without risks since any prolonged interruption of the blood supply to the brain (see below) can cause damage.
It is possible to render someone unconscious by partially strangling them - this is called a sleeper hold, a blood choke or, in judo, a choke hold. It involves compressing both carotid arteries and temporarily shutting off the blood supply to the brain. Ten to fifteen seconds of compression can knock someone out but prolonged force can result in brain damage and even death - see Kathy Reichs' *The Bone Collection* (2016) and Michael Robotham's *Close Your Eyes* (2015) for examples in fiction and Chapter 7 for more details. This is fraught with danger, however, as compression of the vagus nerve can stop the heart - see, for instance, P.D. James' *Cover Her Face* (1962) for an unintended consequence.

Partially strangling someone by compressing their windpipe so their brain is deprived of oxygen can also cause them to lose consciousness temporarily but is also dangerous - permanent damage could result and there is the danger of compressing the vagus nerve as mentioned above.

Writing knockouts:

- Chloroform hardly ever works.
- Remember anaesthetics take time to act and their effects are not usually prolonged.
- Keeping someone unconscious and alive requires advanced medical skills.
- The most reliable way to knock someone out with a drug is to put it in their drink or food but this takes time.
- Most anaesthetic drugs are difficult to obtain but date rape drugs can be obtained from shady sources.
- Gassing groups of people into unconsciousness is not credible except under very unusual circumstances.

- A blow on the head could disorientate someone long enough to administer a drug - but beware of haematomas and brain damage.

- Choke holds and strangulation can be effective if done properly but can cause permanent effects such as death.

- Any period of unconsciousness will have residual effects, for varying periods of time, that would prevent a character from thinking clearly or exerting themselves.

CHAPTER 4: EXPLOSIVES AND EXPLOSIONS

Explosives can be a difficult area for the writer. It is important to be convincing but equally important not to provide too much detail which could enable someone to produce an explosive or construct a bomb. In this chapter I will explain some of the science behind explosives but I will not include recipes or bomb designs for obvious reasons.

What makes an explosive?

Excluding bursting pressure vessels, an explosion usually means the sudden release from a substance of a large volume of gas accompanied by noise, flame and, often, a shock wave. There are two basic types of explosives: low explosives and high explosives and both types involve a sudden and energetic chemical reaction.

Low explosives

The archetypal low explosive is gunpowder (black powder), a mixture of sulfur, charcoal and potassium nitrate (saltpetre) originally invented by the Chinese in the eleventh century. Gunpowder deflagrates - that is, it burns rapidly releasing gas and smoke. The rate at which the flame moves through the powder is relatively slow - below the speed of sound (less than 343 metres per second). This means that there is no shock-wave and a small pile of gunpowder will flare rather than go bang. If confined, for instance in the barrel of a musket, it will produce a "proper" explosion as the gases burst out. Black powder has been superseded by more powerful smokeless propellants in cartridges but is still used in re-enactments of historic battles using old-style weapons. Low explosives are often mixtures of substances, rather than single chemical compounds, usually an oxidising agent (a chemical with available oxygen bound up in its structure such as a chlorate or nitrate) and a fuel, such as carbon, sulfur or a powdered metal.

High explosives

High explosives detonate, which is to say that a shockwave moves through the exploding material faster than the speed of sound - usually thousands of metres per second. They are normally specific compounds rather than mixtures and will explode whether or not they are confined. They need a detonator to set them off (see below). Examples of high explosives are TNT, RDX, C-4 and Semtex.

The most widely used non-military explosive is ANFO - a mixture of ammonium nitrate and fuel oil. This is classified as a blasting agent (it is used principally in mining, quarrying and construction) and will only detonate if a sufficiently powerful booster is used (see below).

Primary, secondary and tertiary explosives

Explosives are also classified by the ease with which they detonate. A primary explosive is sensitive to shock, impact, friction, heat and, sometimes, static electricity. These materials are used to set off secondary explosives and typical uses are in the priming caps of cartridges, blasting caps and detonators. Commonly used compounds include mercury fulminate, lead azide and lead styphnate. The material used to inflate some types airbags in vehicles, sodium azide, is such a compound, producing a large volume of gas, very quickly, when ignited.

Primary explosives are dangerous to handle and transport which is why they are usually moved in small quantities. They can also be dangerous to manufacture so a character in a novel intending to make, say, mercury fulminate would need reasonable chemical skills in order to avoid a potentially fatal accident. Transporting enough through London to blow someone across a room, which one novel featured, would be a seriously bad idea.

A secondary explosive requires a primary explosive to set it off and this is normally in the form of a detonator. This is a small tube containing a primary explosive and may be set off by an electric current or a burning fuse. Most blasting operations use electrically fired detonators as they are predictable - when demolishing a power station chimney, for instance, it is important that the charges go off in the correct order so that the chimney falls where it is supposed to.

Tertiary explosives - blasting agents - need more than a simple detonator to set them off as they are insensitive to shock. They require a booster charge, consisting of a secondary explosive such as a stick of gelignite or dynamite, set off by a conventional detonator to start the explosion. The insensitivity of tertiary explosives makes them particularly safe to transport and use.

Propellants

The materials used in cartridges to propel bullets are known as propellants rather than explosives, although they can be made to explode under certain circumstances. They are designed to burn quickly and smoothly within the weapon so that the projectile experiences a steady - but very fast - acceleration. A small charge of a primary explosive in the back of the cartridge (see Chapter 6) ignites the propellant when the weapon is fired.

Gas explosions

Gas explosions are an unfortunate consequence of using piped gas to provide heat in homes and other buildings. If gas leaks from a pipe into a confined space, such as a room or cellar, it will mix with air until an explosion is possible. When the percentage of gas in the mixture is just enough for an explosion to occur it is said to be at the Lower Explosive Limit. When there is a high percentage of gas and just enough air for an explosion to occur it is said to be at the Higher Explosive Limit. Between these concentrations the gas/air mixture will explode if ignited. The limits vary according to the gas - those for natural gas from a main will not be the same as those for propane from a cylinder.

When a gas/air mixture is between the explosive limits a spark can set off an explosion which is why you should not turn on or off lights or other electrical equipment if you smell gas - virtually all switches create a spark as they operate. TV programmes and films have shown various ways of triggering a gas explosion in a booby-trapped house from a doorbell (*Shameless*[a]) to a central heating timer (*Cracker*[b]). As a plot device this can work since there are many devices in the home which come with timers or could be fitted with one. There is no guarantee that the mixture would be correct but we can gloss over that.

Industrial stores of gases and flammable liquids can give rise to explosions in major accidents (see case study).

Case study: An industrial explosion[1]

> In 2005 fuel was being loaded into a storage tank at the Buncefield fuel depot, Hertfordshire, but faulty equipment led to a major overflow. A series of factors led to a fuel-air explosion as leaking fuel evaporated and the vapour cloud ignited. Twenty fuel tanks were overwhelmed, the noise was heard 125 miles away and the explosions showed up on earthquake monitoring equipment. Amazingly there were no fatalities but 43 people were injured and others in the vicinity suffered from smoke inhalation. Property damage was extensive.

Dust explosions

Fine, dry particles of flammable dust suspended in air form a potentially explosive mixture which can be ignited by a spark, flame or static electricity. This is a risk which operators of grain silos and flour mills must guard against and although not really practical as a murder device it could feature in a plot. In Philip Pullman's *Northern Lights* (1995) a character sets off a dust explosion in a kitchen, using flour, enabling her to escape.

Plastic explosive

A plastic explosive is simply one which can be moulded into specific shapes. This makes it easier to wrap the material around structures for demolition or otherwise mould it to get the blast in the desired direction. It comprises a high explosive such as RDX mixed with liquids which give it the overall texture of modelling clay. Well-known versions are C-4, based on RDX, and Semtex, based on RDX and PETN. Both have civil and military applications and both have been used by terrorists. Semtex, smuggled into the luggage hold, was used to bring down Pan Am Flight 103 over Lockerbie in 1988[2] and C-4 was used by Al Qaeda to attack the American warship USS Cole in 2000[3].

Plastic explosives are generally safe to handle as they are insensitive and require a detonator to set them off. C-4 will even tolerate the impact of a bullet[4]. Plastic explosives cannot easily be made from scratch so, unless your bomb-maker is a skilled chemist with access to a wide range of chemicals, they would have to be stolen. Organised criminal gangs or terrorists will be able to get hold of these materials but an individual member of the public would find it very difficult.

Shaped charges

The blast as a high explosive detonates will normally spread in all directions - if a bomb goes off in mid-air, for instance, the blast front will be spherical. It is possible, however, to focus the force of the explosion by shaping the charge so that much more energy is released in a desired direction. Anti-tank missiles use this effect to punch holes in armour where simply exploding the missile without a shaped charge would do little damage and shaped charges are used widely in the oil industry to extend wells.

Detonating cord

For demolition jobs charges must be detonated in the correct order and at specific intervals. Sophisticated firing programs and electronic controls may be used but an alternative is detonating cord. This is a thin plastic tube filled with PETN which is initiated with a blasting cap. The detonation travels down the cord extremely quickly and will set off many secondary explosives. A booster is needed if it is to be used with ANFO. Detonating cord can also be use as a precise cutting agent when wrapped round cables, pipes and underwater obstructions such as old dock pilings[5].

High explosive or incendiary bomb?

It is important to distinguish between high explosive and incendiary bombs. A high explosive bomb is designed to cause death and damage by means of a blast. An incendiary device, however, is designed to set fire to things and causes very little, if any, blast damage - some authors have confused these two. I would not be writing this if the bomb which landed close to my father during WW2 had been high explosive rather than incendiary. In the civil context, animal rights activists have used many incendiary devices to set fire to property while current terrorist groups use high explosive devices to kill people.

The components of a bomb
An explosive device consists of three main parts: the charge, a detonator or igniter and a triggering device. The charge will usually be a high explosive although a low explosive confined in a rigid container is sometimes used. The detonator for a high explosive could be a commercial device - your character would have to steal it – or, with sufficient skill and access to materials, it could be made at home using a primary explosive. For a confined low explosive, such as black powder or cartridge propellant, an igniting device rather than a detonator could be used. Note that an ANFO bomb will need a booster as well as a detonator.

The triggering device could be a simple burning fuse but electrically-fired detonators or igniters are far more common. These require a power source such as a battery and can be set off either remotely or using a timer. Remote detonation can be achieved using wires leading from the device to a nearby location, as in some IEDs deployed against military personnel in Iraq and Afghanistan, or by radio or a mobile phone. Some knowledge of electronics, and access to components, would be needed if your character is to set off a bomb using a mobile phone or radio. Timing devices vary from the simple, such as an alarm clock with contacts fixed to the hands and face, to the complex, involving digital electronics. Electronic timer modules can be purchased freely but some skills would be needed to use them. The big display which bleeps menacingly and counts down to zero in thrillers is usually there for dramatic effect.

A different type of triggering device is the mercury tilt switch. This is a tube containing a bead of mercury which moves downwards and completes an electrical circuit when the switch is tilted. Such a device was used by terrorists to murder the MP Airey Neave at the House of Commons in 1979[6] and Peter James features one in *Love You Dead* (2016).

Any simple switch can be used to complete a circuit and trigger a bomb. Booby traps can be triggered by small switches which operate when something pushes against or moves them. A hand-held switch (referred to as a detonator on occasions) is used by suicide bombers and some designs (dead man's switches) detonate the bomb when they are released, rather than pressed, so shooting the terrorist will not prevent the bomb from going off. The TV series *Bodyguard*[c] featured such a device.

Handling and defusing

Sophisticated terrorist bombs may be fitted with anti-handling devices which cause the bomb to go off when handled or attempts are made to defuse it. These are unlikely to be present in the sort of device used by an amateur bomb-maker so it would be credible for the heroine or hero to neutralise the device without being blown up. Carefully pulling the detonator out and moving it clear of the rest of the bomb would prevent a full-scale explosion even if the detonator fired. Simply disconnecting the battery could make the device relatively safe, although shock could still set off the detonator and a simple device using a parallel circuit could still fire it. Dropping the whole bomb in a bucket of water could, with certain designs, set it off if the battery was still connected and water completed the firing circuit. A bomb based on nitroglycerine would be very dangerous to touch and should be left to the experts. I must emphasise that these are things your character could do in fiction - should you ever have the misfortune to come close to a bomb in real life, **don't touch it!**

Grenades

Grenades are small, hand-thrown bombs designed to kill or maim anyone within a reasonably small radius or in a room. One of the oldest type, the Mills bomb, was developed in the First World War and its cast iron casing was shaped like a pineapple. This enabled it to split easily into pieces when the device exploded, hurling lethal shrapnel in all directions. More modern devices are shaped differently from the Mills bomb but the basic principle is the same. Pulling a pin enables a lever to spring upwards when the grenade is thrown. This lets a spring-loaded plunger inside the device strike a percussion cap which ignites a fuse. Some seconds later the fuse sets off a detonator and the grenade explodes.

I mention grenades because they are being smuggled into the U.K. and could end up in the hands of criminal gangs or terrorists. According to the National Crime Agency they have a street value of £250 to £750 and they seized 17 in the first four months of 2018, 13 of which were likely to work[7].

The effects of explosions

The consequences of an explosion depend on the amount and nature of the explosive, where it is detonated, whether shrapnel generating items are added, surrounding materials and, of course, the number of people in the vicinity and how close they are.

The first effect of a high explosive detonation is a blast wave - a zone of very high pressure moving supersonically outwards from the site of the explosion. Fragments of the bomb casing and surrounding materials will be thrown outwards and more debris will be created as the blast wave hits structures, especially windows. Secondly, the explosion creates a vacuum in the immediate area so air rushes back to fill this, carrying debris with it. This is known as the blast wind[8]. Depending on the composition of the explosive, a fireball may be created and heat radiated outwards. Heated rising air may create a familiar mushroom-shaped cloud - large conventional explosions can cause this as well as nuclear weapons. Low explosives don't produce a supersonic blast wave but will cause a blast wind and throw fragments about.

The effects of a blast on the human body are divided into four categories. Primary injuries only occur with high explosives and result from the high-pressure blast wave. Hollow structures are most at risk including the lungs, inner ears, large intestine and eyes. Concussion from the shock to the brain also occurs. Secondary injuries result from flying debris and bomb fragments, striking and penetrating whichever parts of the body get in the way. Tertiary injuries are caused when the victim is thrown about by the blast wind and include fractures, amputations and brain injuries. Quaternary injuries comprise any other type of damage including burns, crushing and longer-term effects such as asthma and other conditions affecting the lungs. Of particular concern is the condition known as "blast lung" where potentially fatal damage to the lungs occurs, sometimes without obvious external trauma[9].

Whatever type of explosive is used, anyone close by will suffer from tinnitus and possibly permanent hearing loss. The extent of damage potentially caused to the brain by blast is still not completely understood[10].

Damage to buildings will depend on the type and amount of explosive used, where it is placed and the strength of the structure, the weakest points being affected first. Industrial premises where explosions are possible may be fitted with explosion relief panels or a lightweight roof which can blow out in the event of an accident, allowing the blast to escape in a safe direction without bringing the whole building down[11]. This is not a feature of normal buildings so one building blowing up could result in damage to those adjacent - and windows will be shattered over a wide area. Other possible effects include broken gas mains (which may cause fires) power cuts, telecommunication disruptions and burst water mains.

The aftermath of an explosion may involve fires and structural weaknesses in buildings which will make them dangerous to enter. Dust clouds may persist for some time and may include toxic materials such as asbestos if older buildings are involved. Long-term lung damage was reported in the firefighters who attended the 9/11 site, caused by the inhalation of toxic materials released from the structure of the buildings. Toxic gases are also a feature of many explosions but these can dissipate fairly quickly. Explosives may generate a large amount of heat but not all do - TATP, used by the July 2005 bombers in London[12], does not.

Shrapnel

As noted above, the fragments of a bomb casing fly out at speed and can cause death or serious injury. Terrorists often enhance the lethal potential of their devices by including nails and other metal items to maximise the damage done to people.

Case study: Shrapnel in Soho[13]

> On 30th April 1999 a nail bomb exploded without warning at the Admiral Duncan pub, a gay venue, in Soho. Two people were killed and a further 81 were injured. It followed a previous nail bomb in Brixton which injured 39 people and a blast in Brick Lane in London's East End. An extreme right-wing group claimed responsibility for these attacks which were homophobic and racially motivated

Nuclear explosives

Mention must be made of nuclear explosives since they feature, from time to time, in thrillers. The basis of nuclear bombs is the process of nuclear fission which means the splitting of the inner cores (nuclei) of the atoms of certain heavy elements. As this occurs energy is released together with particles which split further nuclei in a chain reaction. All this happens in a tiny fraction of a second and the release of energy is enormous.

Two materials are used as nuclear explosives: plutonium and highly enriched uranium. Plutonium is produced in nuclear reactors and must be separated from other, highly radioactive, materials. Highly enriched uranium is produced from natural uranium by a complicated and energy-intensive process requiring industrial-scale machinery. No terrorist group is able to produce either of these materials but there are concerns that supplies, particularly of enriched uranium, may have been stolen from inadequately monitored establishments in the chaos which followed the collapse of the Soviet Union.

Constructing a credible nuclear weapon would be beyond the reach of a criminal gang or crazed individual and most terrorist groups would have severe difficulties. Much more credible is the idea of a radiation weapon - a dirty bomb. Conventional explosives are needed to set off a nuclear device so even if a nuclear chain reaction did not occur in an improvised bomb, radioactive material would be scattered over a wide area. More likely, however, is a terrorist device using explosives to disperse radioactive materials from the numerous sources used in health care and industry. Radioactive sources are kept securely but could be stolen and are occasionally misplaced. A relatively small explosive charge wrapped round such a source could render a substantial area of a city uninhabitable for many years. Handling such material without proper protection would be highly dangerous but, in the age of the suicide bomber, this would not present a terrorist with a problem.

Individual explosives

It is worth mentioning some specific explosives, as well as those covered above, and their characteristics although some of them are unlikely to figure in "regular" crime fiction.

- **Gunpowder** (black powder) is a simple mixture of chemicals which combine to form a deflagrating (low) explosive. It can be made in the home but a key ingredient, potassium nitrate, is now restricted (see below). People involved in Civil War battle re-enactments and similar can purchase and keep black powder, for use in antique weapons, with an Explosives Certificate from the police.

- **Chlorate** mixtures are low explosives consisting of either sodium or potassium chlorate,which provide oxygen, mixed with a fuel such as sugar, sulfur or a powdered metal. Sodium chlorate weedkiller and sugar mix tures were popular with adventurous schoolboys making fireworks until the weedkiller first had a fire suppressant added and was then withdrawn altogether. Potassium chlorate has been used as an oxygenating compound for home aquaria and Peter James used this in *Love You Dead* (2016).

  A strong acid will ignite a mixture containing a chlorate and the erosion of a rubber balloon or condom by sulfuric acid has been used as a timing device for bombs[14]. Both sodium and potassium chlorate are now restricted.

- **Dynamite** is a powerful explosive consisting of nitroglyc erine absorbed by an inert material such as clay or a type of earth. This was the first explosive more powerful than black powder which could be handled safely and is still widely used in mining, quarrying, demolition and construction. It is set off using a simple detonator, needing no booster, but in some conditions it can "sweat" liquid nitroglycerine which makes it highly sensitive and prone to accidental detonation.

- **Gelignite** is a high explosive composition based on nitro-cellulose mixed with nitroglycerine, or nitroglycol, and wood pulp plus saltpetre. It is cheap, powerful and reasonably safe to handle, needing a detonator to cause it to explode. Gelignite is widely used in blasting and, like dynamite, is sometimes used as a booster for ANFO charges. It has been used illicitly by terrorists, from Ireland and elsewhere[15], and also by safecrackers.

- **Hydrogen peroxide** is not, of itself, an explosive although concentrated solutions can decompose suddenly and dramatically, especially if heated. It is a raw material for the manufacture of TATP and HMTD, however, and is a powerful oxidising agent. This means that a moderately concentrated solution can form a potentially explosive mixture with a fuel such as flour. One such mixture was used in a failed bomb attack in London in 2005, two weeks after the bus bombings[16]. Hydrogen peroxide, at lower concentrations, has legitimate uses as a bleach for hair and a disinfectant but is completely different from the chlorine bleaches used as toilet disinfectants. It is important not to get the two types confused if you are writing about an amateur bomb-maker.

- **Mercury fulminate** is a primary explosive which was widely used in primers for cartridges and detonators until more stable and reliable compounds superseded it. Preparing mercury fulminate is not very difficult although two of the raw materials are now restricted in the U.K. - mercury, as it is poisonous, and nitric acid as it is an explosives precursor. Mercury fulminate explodes easily on exposure to shock, friction and heat which is why it is both useful and dangerous to handle in any quantity.

- **Nitroglycerine** is a highly sensitive, high explosive liquid which is used as a component of other explosives, such as dynamite and gelignite, and cartridge propellants such as double-base smokeless powders and, formerly, cordite. In small doses the chemical is also used to treat angina. Its manufacture is a simple but highly dangerous activity - operatives in nitroglycerine plants used to perch on one-legged stools to prevent them from nodding off while watching the process. With access to the raw materials and some chemical knowledge an amateur could make it at home, but this would be very risky!

- **RDX** is a high explosive, with military and civilian applications, used as a component of the plastic explosives Semtex and C-4. It is stable and highly resistant to shock, requiring a detonator to explode it. RDX was used widely in the second world war, alone or in mixtures, as it is much more powerful than TNT, the main explosive up untill then. Its manufacture is not that complicated but requires some unpleasant and restricted substances so it is not really feasible for an amateur to make it. Terrorists have used RDX, in Semtex or on its own, in numerous attacks around the world.

- **TATP, triacetone triperoxide**, is a moderately powerful explosive which is a favourite with terrorists. It is easy to make from ingredients which were, until recently, readily available although its manufacture is haz ardous and accidental detonations are a constant threat, hence its alternative name, Mother of Satan. The dry substance is also sensitive to shock and friction. Hydrogen peroxide, a key ingredient, is only available to the general public at low concentrations but it would be possible to concentrate it to the level more suitable for TATP manufacture with a modicum of chemical knowl edge and some cheap equipment. TATP has been used in bomb attacks in London, Paris, Brussels, Manchester, Surabaya and Sri Lanka[17], on occasions together with HMTD (hexamethylene triperoxide diamine), a more sensitive but easy to prepare primary explosive.

- **TNT, trinitrotoluene**, is a shock-resistant high explosive which has been in use for military and civil purposes since the beginning of the twentieth century. It is still in widespread use in mining, demolition and military applications. TNT can be melted safely and poured into shells and will burn quietly without exploding if uncon fined. It normally needs a booster to detonate it and is often used in mixtures with other compounds, such as ammonium nitrate, to provide a greater explosive power. A TNT explosion releases a cloud of black smoke as not all the carbon in the material is converted to gas. It is not easy to make, involving some dangerous mate rials, hence a criminal planning to use it would have to steal some and also obtain a suitable detonating system.

Detection

Many explosives contain a combination of atoms within their molecules called the nitro group. This is easy to detect by means of sniffer dogs and monitoring instruments, e.g. at airports. The nitro group is not exclusive to explosives, however, as the wrongly convicted Birmingham Six found to their cost. They had played cards on a train and traces of nitrocellulose from the cards were transferred to their hands. Sloppy forensic work[18] meant that they were wrongly identified as having handled the explosives which blew up a bar in the centre of Birmingham.

Other types of explosive - RDX for instance - are less easy to spot with monitors but there are more sophisticated devices now available to do this. All plastic explosives must now have, by law, an ingredient included in their composition (a taggant) which makes them easier to detect and also to trace them back to their place of origin. Batches of Semtex made before 1990 did not have this safety feature[19]. Packaged plastic explosives must also have details of their origin included on the wrapping.

Legal issues
It is illegal, in the U.K., to make, keep and store explosives without the appropriate permissions. The law is complex but, in brief, for most explosives you need an Explosives Certificate from the police to acquire and keep them - this includes black powder, as noted above. You must not be "of unsound mind or intemperate habit" or be a prohibited person and must provide a good reason for having the explosives[20].

For certain aspects of storage, a licence from either the local authority or the Health and Safety Executive is required. It is technically possible, however, to purchase and keep smoke-less powder for reloading firearm cartridges without any kind of permit although sellers normally ask to see a copy of a relevant firearms or shotgun certificate. If you are buying primers for metallic cartridges you do need a firearms certificate for the relevant weapon and ammunition.

Certain chemicals which can be used to make explosives, and some poisons, are subject to the Control of Poisons and Explosives Precursors Regulations 2015 as described in Chapter 1. The table below shows which explosives precursors are regulated and which are reportable and gives the threshold concentrations at which the law applies. Note that mercury, and one of its compounds which can also be used to make explosives, is regulated under the poisons provisions.

Controlled explosives precursors[21]

Regulated substances	Reportable substances
Hydrogen peroxide:12% w/w	Ammonium nitrate
Nitromethane: 30% w/w	Acetone
Nitric acid: 3% w/w	Hexamine
Sodium chlorate: 40% w/w	Potassium nitrate
Sulfuric acid 15% w/w	Sodium nitrate
Potassium chlorate: 40% w/w	Calcium nitrate
Sodium perchlorate: 40% w/w	Calcium ammonium nitrate
Potassium perchlorate: 40% w/w	

Anti-terrorism legislation is also relevant - the Terrorism Act 2006 prohibits the preparing for a terrorist act as well as the preparation of any radioactive device (e.g. a dirty bomb). The Act also prohibits the dissemination of a publication which includes information useful in the preparation or commission of an act of terrorism. This would apply, presumably, to distributing terrorist bomb-making manuals rather than thrillers and chemistry textbooks.

It is also an offence to collect or possess information likely to be useful to a terrorist and the Counter-Terrorism and Border Security Act 2019 makes it illegal to view material likely to be of use to a terrorist online. As with previous provisions, there is a "reasonable excuse defence" which applies to journalists and academics who need to research such material. Whether this defence applies to crime writers remains to be seen but it is advisable to be cautious when researching.[22]

Availability and practicality

The days when the general public could purchase materials to make their own fireworks and explosives at home are long gone. Licences and explosives certificates are not handed out without thorough checks and setting up a home laboratory is not a simple matter. Even experienced chemists carrying on experiments at home have attracted the attention of the authorities[23].

It may be possible for your protagonist to buy a reportable substance such as ammonium nitrate fertiliser - although someone who looks nothing like a farmer would attract suspicion - but commercial blasting explosives are tightly restricted.

So how can your character get hold of materials to make a credible bomb? The obvious answer is to steal them but security around explosives is tight.

Someone with access to a laboratory, and sufficient chemical knowledge, could get hold of raw materials and make their own. There is the possibility of someone who legitimately holds black powder, smokeless powders or ingredients for pyrotechnics "going rogue" and using them for nefarious purposes.

It may also be possible for someone with laboratory skills to buy restricted explosives precursors at lower concentrations, so that the regulations don't apply, and then concentrate them to more useful levels but this could be dangerous depending on the substance.
Organised criminals and gangs can, of course, obtain explosives through theft or smuggling.

Case study: Bombs in Devon[24]

In 2018 Steven Bracher, a resident of Bishops Tawton in Devon, was jailed for possessing explosive substances including 9kg of ANFO. A routine search at a pharmacy, where he was collecting a prescribed controlled drug, led to the discovery of a white powder. When police were called he was found to have a tube containing black powder in his possession. Bracher was arrested and in his flat police found 17 small bombs and a tub of ANFO. Experts testified that any of Bracher's small bombs would be sufficiently powerful to set off the ANFO. Although he was reported to be a racist and homophobic bigot, Bracher was not charged as a terrorist since there was no evidence that he intended to harm anyone with his devices.

Writing explosives:

- Avoid giving too much detail on explosive manufacture or bomb making. For clear information on what you can include in a story, there is no substitute for professional legal advice.

- Be careful not to confuse incendiaries with high explosive devices.

- Don't confuse primary, secondary and tertiary explosives and note the need for booster charges in some cases.

- Note the damage which can be caused to people who are close to an explosion, from tinnitus to dismemberment.

- Many explosives are sensitive and dangerous to handle or transport. Untrained users could easily blow themselves up.

- Be aware of the difficulties the ordinary person faces in attempting to obtain explosives or their precursors.

CHAPTER 5: FIRES

Deliberate fires feature frequently in crime novels as a means of murder, a method of destroying evidence, an attack on property or all three. Approximately 20% of fires attended by U.K. fire and rescue services are known or thought to be deliberate[1]. I do not propose to describe in detail novel methods of setting fires - basic arson techniques are simple - but there are some unusual ways in which things can catch fire to which I will allude. I will also point out some mistakes which are sometimes made in print and on screen.

The fire triangle and tetrahedron

Fire is a process of oxidation - the elements of a flammable material combine with oxygen, in the air or from chemicals called oxidising agents, to produce heat, light and combustion products. In the majority of cases the burning material, be it coal or your sofa, will contain carbon and the combustion products will include carbon dioxide and, usually, carbon monoxide. Other substances will also be produced and these are discussed below. The flammable material is referred to as the fuel. This gives us two sides of what is referred to as the fire triangle - fuel and oxygen. The third side is heat which is needed to ignite the mixture and this could take the form of a flame, heat released from a chemical or physical process or a spark. All three sides of the fire triangle must be present if a fire is to start and fire prevention aims to prevent them coming together.

Once the fire has started, a fourth factor is required which changes the fire triangle into a fire tetrahedron. This factor is a self-sustaining chemical chain reaction, i.e. a means by which the fire can continue to burn and spread. In simple terms, the heat produced as the fire starts ignites more combustible material which goes on to ignite more, and so on, always assuming that there is sufficient oxygen present to allow this. Chemicals called free radicals are produced as materials burn and these are highly effective at igniting fuels.

Some fire extinguishers, notably those safe to use on electrical fires, work, in part, by mopping up free radicals and halting the chain reaction. Water based extinguishers work by cooling the fire down while foam and carbon dioxide extinguishers work mainly by excluding oxygen. Carbon dioxide extinguishers are suitable for most small fires, including electrical ones. Water-based devices should not be used on electrical fires as the operator could receive an electric shock. Foam extinguishers are used on burning liquids such as petrol.

Smoulder versus flame

Flames are, essentially, burning gases, usually with glowing particles carried within them. Materials which burn in flames do so as they are heated to a sufficiently high temperature to break down and produce vapours which then ignite. Most fires are like this. Smouldering fires, on the other hand, simply glow as combustion takes place on the solid surface of the fuel and spread as the unburnt material ahead of the combustion front is heated to the point at which it ignites. Such fires can be started by low temperature ignition sources (see below) and can convert to flaming fires as heat output rises and gaseous breakdown products are formed. It takes 30 minutes or more for smouldering foam padded furniture, ignited by a lit cigarette, to burst into flame[2]. Some materials will not smoulder - many plastics will simply melt if touched with a lit cigarette - but those which form a rigid char (a solid consisting mainly of carbon) on burning may do so. Smouldering fires tend to produce much more smoke than flaming fires and damage is usually severe but localised. Flaming fire damage tends to be more widespread and superficial.

A smouldering fire can transition to a flaming fire if oxygen levels increase and the combustion temperature rises. Blowing air onto a glowing ember can cause it to burst into flame while smoking a cigarette around a leaking oxygen cylinder could cause the cigarette to flare up, with dramatic consequences. (If including this in a plot, please don't say that the oxygen catches fire or is flammable).

Ignition

Gases and vapours are relatively easy to ignite if mixed in the correct proportions with air i.e. between the upper and lower flammability limits (analogous to the explosive limits described in Chapter 4). If there is too much fuel in the mixture it will not burn and nor will it do so if there is not enough. Even so, sufficient energy must be supplied either in the form of heat or a spark. The ignition source heats a small volume of the gas/air mixture to a critical temperature, called the autoignition temperature, at which point it catches fire and the flame spreads to the rest of the gas. If this temperature is not reached, or the spark is not powerful enough, ignition won't occur. Petrol stations display signs prohibiting mobile phone use in the belief that the tiny spark which occurs when they are used could ignite petrol vapour. This is a fallacy - there is not enough energy in the spark, even if the correct fuel/air mixture could penetrate the casing of the phone. Fires do sometimes occur at petrol stations from sparks but the sparks in question come from static electricity build-up on people[3].

Case Study: Sparking cat[4]

An unusual case of a spark igniting gas happened in New York in 1922 where an iron tank of coal gas (the mixture of hydrogen and carbon monoxide used for heating and lighting prior to the introduction of natural gas) was used to kill unwanted cats. Static electricity had built up on the fur of one cat and when he was dropped in the tank it created a spark which led to a gas/air explosion, injuring three people and scattering dead cats around the premises.

Liquids such as petrol, diesel and white spirit will ignite if there is sufficient vapour at the surface to form a flammable mixture with air. Below a certain temperature, called the flashpoint, not enough vapour is released to allow ignition. You could hold a lighted candle over a bucket of diesel (flashpoint more than 55°C) forever at room temperature and it would not ignite. Do the same over a bucket of petrol (flashpoint around -43°C) and the result would be very different. Liquids whose flashpoints are above room temperature can be ignited if they are soaked onto something which can act as a wick. A flame (not a spark) will vaporise a portion of the liquid, forming a flammable mixture with air, and the heat produced as this burns will vaporise more liquid which is drawn through the wick. Thus an oil-soaked rag will burn readily while a pool of oil will not.

Solids can only be ignited when they are heated to a temperature sufficient to produce flammable breakdown products (more correctly called pyrolysis products) as noted above. For many materials, such as wood and various common plastics, the required temperature is between 150°C and 500°C.

Note that a flame or spark is not needed if a mixture of gas/vapour and air is heated to its autoignition temperature by other means. A small amount of petrol in a sealed drum, otherwise full of air, heated by an external fire would ignite when this temperature is reached - and, being confined, would cause the drum to explode. Too much petrol would produce a mixture above the higher flammability limit and would not ignite, and neither would a full drum. If the full drum burst as a result of increased pressure caused by expanding vapour within, the vapour cloud would flare up once it mixed with sufficient air and hit the external fire, also igniting any liquid petrol. On a large scale this can cause an explosion known as a BLEVE - Boiling Liquid Expanding Vapour Explosion.

For the sake of completeness it is worth mentioning a couple of other means of ignition. In a petrol (or LPG) fuelled car a spark is needed to ignite the mixture of atomised petrol (or gas) and air in the cylinder but diesel engines need no spark. The mixture of diesel and air is compressed sharply and this causes the temperature to rise above the autoignition point (over 250°C). You may have noticed a similar, although less extreme, phenomenon when you pump up a bicycle tyre - the part of the pump where the air is compressed gets hot. Friction can also cause ignition - starting campfires by rubbing sticks together or rapidly rotating the end of a stick in a hole in a piece of wood surrounded by tinder is an example while inadequately lubricated bearings can cause fires in machinery.

Spontaneous combustion

Some things can ignite spontaneously in air: they are said to be pyrophoric. Bulk stores of coal, grain, hay and other organic materials can self-heat as they undergo slow oxidation in the air. The heat can build up within the material until it starts to burn. Some finely powdered metals are pyrophoric - uranium and titanium are examples - and various organic compounds will also behave in this way. Tom Bale, in *Each Little Lie* (2017) used tert-butyllithium as an igniter for an accelerant. In real life this pyrophoric chemical caused a fire which fatally burned a researcher at the University of California, Los Angeles[5]. Such chemicals are hard to obtain and dangerous to handle, so would not be readily usable by an amateur fire raiser. Certain types of oil, if spread thinly on rags or paper towels, may also generate enough heat to ignite as they oxidise and the long, slow pyrolysis of wood in the absence of air can, under certain circumstances, produce a pyrophoric carbon char[6].

Spontaneous combustion of human beings has been reported and has also been used in fiction - the character of Krook in Charles Dickens' *Bleak House* (1853) was reported to have died by spontaneously catching fire. A closer examination of the phenomenon provides a more logical explanation. A small fire, e.g. clothing ignited by a cigarette, melts subcutaneous body fat which seeps out into cloth that then acts as a wick. The fat continues to burn, just as wax does around a candle wick, producing localised high temperatures which are sufficient to reduce much of the body to ash[7]. The fire need not spread - although there would be much greasy smoke emitted - unless there was combustible material nearby. This is a highly unusual phenomenon but it was used in an episode of the B.B.C. TV series *New Tricks*[a].

Finally, some mixtures of chemicals can self-ignite without an external source of energy as reactions between components generate heat. The effect of acids on chlorates was mentioned in Chapter 4 and highly concentrated sulfuric acid can, under certain circumstances, cause organic materials such as sugar to catch fire. Adding glycerine to potassium permanganate will result in the mixture igniting within a few minutes, a plot device used in Peter O'Donnell's Modesty Blaise novel *Last Day in Limbo* (1976). If potassium permanganate is involved, elevated levels of manganese at the point of origin will point to deliberate fire-starting - assuming someone analyses the debris. Solid peroxides, such as sodium peroxide, must be kept away from combustible materials lest they cause them to catch fire.

Water added to some highly reactive chemicals can also start a fire. Sodium or potassium metal dropped into water will generate hydrogen which explodes when the temperature of the reaction reaches its ignition point. On a small scale, this used to be a popular demonstration in school chemistry laboratories. Moisture will also cause tert-butyllithium and similar compounds to ignite.

Fire development

Once a fire has started it will spread as long as the conditions of the fire tetrahedron are met. Heat transferred to nearby combustible materials will raise them to ignition temperature. Hot combustion gases and smoke will rise by convection as they are less dense than the surrounding air so the fire will spread faster vertically than horizontally. This means that in the absence of obstructions, or airflow affecting the movement of flames, the fire will take on a conical shape and a flat vertical surface such as a wall will exhibit a v-shaped pattern of damage[8]. A consequence of this, for someone inside a burning room, is that there will be a supply of relatively cool and clean air at floor level for a while. This may provide a few vital seconds for escape - provided that the temperature in the room is not lethally hot - but eventually the smoke layer will reach the ground.

At this stage the fire is fuel-limited. Rising flames from a low-level fire in a room will hit the ceiling and be rapidly deflected along its surface, spreading the fire much faster than the fire at floor level. This can cause pilot fires on the floor where, for instance, light fittings or curtains catch fire some distance away from the original fire and fall to the floor, igniting the carpet and other flammable materials[9]. This phenomenon is also known as dropdown.

As the fire continues to burn the smoke layer will thicken and get hotter, radiating a large amount of heat. This will heat up other flammable materials in the room, causing them to break down and release flammable gases and vapours. When these ignite, almost simultaneously, the fire will grow extremely rapidly - a state known as flashover which can occur within five minutes in a domestic fire, depending on what is in the room[10]. Flashover does not always occur - if there is insufficient fuel or ventilation in the room, the rate of heat release is too slow, or too much of the heat and gases escape from the room it will not happen.

After flashover, when most combustible material in the room is alight, the fully-developed fire burns steadily and is said to be ventilation limited - its rate of burning depends on how much air gets into the room. In areas around doors or windows where air can get in, burning will be fiercer and more damage will be caused. The fire will spread as flames and hot gases escape from the room and contact other flammable materials. Particularly effective at spreading fire is the chimney effect - the flames and hot gases will rise up a shaft such as a stairwell in the same way that smoke from a fireplace rises up a chimney, causing considerable damage to upper floors[11]. On a smaller scale, if the windows in a burning upper room are broken and air can enter the house from below, the fire in the room will tend to intensify as more air is sucked in.

An extreme version of this is the flashback or backdraft (U.S. term). Here, ventilation is poor but there is plenty of fuel and heat so pyrolysis generates a high concentration of hot vapour and combustible gases in the room. When a firefighter breaks a window or smashes down a door the sudden ingress of air can lead to an explosion[12]. For this reason a door which feels hot should not be opened.

Once most of the combustible material in a room is burnt the fire will die down (decay). It may continue to smoulder for some time although it could flare up again. This is particularly the case where the fire has converted from a flaming fire to a smoulder as oxygen levels have been depleted - a fresh influx of air could set it off again. Firefighters will damp down a fire scene even though there may be no flames or obvious smouldering present.

Effects of fire on buildings
Even a small fire can cause considerable damage to property as a result of the smoke emitted. Indeed, this damage may spread to adjacent properties, through gaps in party walls in lofts and under floorboards, even though the fire is contained in the

original building. In some older terraced properties there are no dividing walls in the roof space and a fire can spread along the whole terrace with ease. Smoke damage can be cleaned up, albeit with some difficulty, but an intense and prolonged fire can seriously damage the structure of a building.

An obvious type of structural damage is burnt out roof timbers which may no longer support the weight of slates or tiles. Upper floors may be unsupported where joists have been destroyed or weakened. Plastic and lead pipes will have melted, causing gas and water leaks which will have to be repaired before the scene can be examined. Stonework may be weakened by a serious fire and collapse unexpectedly while walls may lean dangerously and cease to support upper floors[13].

A building which has been the site of a serious fire is a dangerous place. There may be asbestos, sharp items sticking out of surfaces, live electrical cables and toxic chemicals present as well as the structural hazards described above. A fire investigator will not go into a fire damaged property unless a thorough safety assessment has been carried out, possibly involving a structural engineer. This will take time and the scene where the detective enters a still-smoking building to look for clues or examine a corpse would not happen.

Effects on people

Most people dying in fires do not burn to death. Sometimes a flash fire will kill a person by burning but in most cases combustion gases are the lethal agent. Chief among these is carbon monoxide, the effects of which are described in Chapter 2. Some synthetic materials, such as nylon and polyurethane, also release hydrogen cyanide when they burn and certain plastics may produce phosgene. These gases are rarely the main cause of death since carbon monoxide is present in much greater quantities[14]. A further factor is the depletion of oxygen in the air - a fire burning in an enclosed space will rapidly use up the available oxygen. Starting a fire in an underground chamber in order to facilitate an escape or attract attention is a seriously bad idea, not just because of the combustion gases produced.

People exposed to a fire may suffer some longer-term effects. Carbon monoxide takes time to clear from the blood once a normal air supply is restored so survivors should always be checked over by a paramedic - or by a doctor in serious cases. Smoke is an irritant and may carry toxic chemicals within it, while inhaling hot gases may badly damage the airways. People with asthma, other lung diseases or heart problems will be particularly at risk. The scenario where a character rescues someone from a burning building, coughs a bit, then dashes off to fight the villain in a prolonged punch-up is medically improbable. Firefighters use self-contained breathing apparatus and heat-resistant clothing for a reason - a wet towel held over the face is no substitute although it is better than nothing. It may filter out larger smoke particles but it will do nothing to prevent the inhalation of carbon monoxide.

Fire has been used to cover up murder, certainly in fiction. The presence or absence of smoke in the airways and the levels of carbon monoxide in the blood are key indicators. If there is smoke present and carbon monoxide levels are high the victim was alive while the fire was burning. If the converse applies the victim was probably dead beforehand, although in some instances - rapid flash fires - they may have been killed by the heat and flames before inhaling significant amounts of these substances[15].

Fire investigation

Investigating the causes of fires is a highly specialist area. The fire and rescue service has a statutory duty to investigate and report on fires while crime scene investigators will be involved if a fire seems suspicious. In complex cases a forensic scientist specialising in fire will be needed. A police detective will be able to add little to the expertise possessed by these people and a pathologist will only be concerned with examining bodies found at the scene, contrary to the impression given in some television programmes.

Once the scene has been declared safe, the fire investigator will attempt to determine where and how a fire started, how it spread, whether an accelerant was used, what factors affected the spread of the fire, whether fire protection equipment was disabled or faulty, and how future fires may be prevented through improved health and safety procedures.

Finding the seat of the fire is a crucial part of this work. The v-shaped pattern of damage noted above is a good indicator, bearing in mind that this may be distorted by local factors. In some cases, an inverted v-shape may be produced when a small amount of fuel is involved next to a wall and the fire does not spread up it - examples are a burning wastepaper bin or a small pool of flammable liquid[16].

In accidental fires there will usually be only one point, or area, of origin. Arson becomes a highly probable cause if there is more than one, and particularly if lines of damage where accelerant has been dripped across the floor, called trailers, link several sites. Pilot fires (dropdown) can confuse the issue but an experienced fire investigator will be able to tell the difference.

Investigators will look out for anything suspicious or out of place, such as:

- An unusual type or quantity of flammable material stored on the premises or left in odd places.
- Filing cabinet drawers left open to enable documents to burn.
- The presence of incendiary devices (see below).
- Residues of accelerants.
- Measures taken to improve ventilation and thus the spread of fire (windows and doors jammed open or ceilings and partition walls damaged).
- The removal of valuable or sentimentally important items such as expensive furniture, jewellery, artworks and pets.

External evidence could include the financial position of the owner of the premises, a history of insurance claims, a pattern of similar fires elsewhere, especially where someone has been convicted of arson and subsequently released, and motives for arson in the owner's relatives or acquaintances.

Accelerants

An accelerant is any material used to start and increase the spread of a fire. Petrol is the commonest example but other flammable liquids such as paraffin (kerosene) or white spirit can be used. If an accelerant has been used, traces of it can sometimes be detected by smell - if not by humans then by specialist dogs trained to detect solvents and liquid fuels.

Accelerants can produce characteristic signs, such as localised burn patterns with sharp curved edges and burning at low levels within the fire-damaged areas where a typical v-shaped pattern would be expected[17]. Some melted burning plastics can mimic accelerants so the only definitive proof that an accelerant was present is laboratory analysis of samples collected at the scene. Even if chemical analyses are positive, it does not mean that arson was committed: there could be a perfectly innocent explanation for the presence of the material.

The analysis of residues can confidently identify the type of accelerant used, discriminating between petrol, white spirit and paraffin (no-one sensible would consider using diesel as an accelerant). These products are complex mixtures of chemicals and sophisticated equipment is needed to identify them.

In some crime stories residues of petrol at a fire scene have been matched to petrol in a suspect's possession as both samples contained the same components in the same proportions. This may have been possible, to some extent, in the past where petrol formulations were changing and the various oil companies adapted to the withdrawal of lead additives from petrol. It is no longer credible, firstly because the heat from the fire would change the proportions of the components present, so they would not match unheated fuel very closely, and also because petrol formulations are much more standardised and individual batches differ little from each other.

It may be possible to identify a brand because of proprietary additives included in the mix but even that is not reliable as petrol from one producer may end up being sold by another[18].

Supermarkets will buy their petrol on the open market and a different manufacturer may be used from week to week. Bear in mind, however, that if samples do not match in the slightest (e.g. if the suspect possessed two-stroke fuel for an outboard motor but the fire was started with ordinary petrol) this could be an indication of innocence - valuable information in itself.

Petrol is an efficient accelerant as it is readily available and, unlike paraffin, does not need a wick to start it burning. It produces a cloud of vapour at room temperature which is easily ignited. An arsonist striking a match to light a pool of petrol would be likely to suffer burns when the vapour bursts into flame - indirect evidence of accelerant use if the person concerned is identified as a suspect.

Finally, it must be remembered that using accelerants - or starting any fire - can have unpredictable results. A drunken arsonist pouring petrol through a letterbox as an act of revenge or intimidation is unlikely to realise that fires can spread faster and less predictably than intended - particularly if the criminal's knowledge of house fires comes only from inaccurate portrayals on popular television soaps. The case study below provides a chilling example.

Case study: Tragedy in Derby[19]

In 2012 Mick Philpott, together with his wife and a friend, conspired to frame his ex-partner for arson by setting fire to the family home in Allenton, Derby (U.K.). He placed a ladder adjacent to his children's bedroom window, so he could act the hero by rescuing them, and then poured accelerant through the letterbox. When lit, the accelerant flared up much faster than expected, engulfing the house before Philpott could come to the rescue. All six children died of smoke inhalation, five at the scene and one later in hospital. Philpott was sent down for life and the others also received long sentences.

Incendiary devices

A range of devices can be used to start fires maliciously and some are much the same as those described for setting off explosions in Chapter 4. Anything which can produce a flame or large spark, capable of igniting a mixture of gas or flammable vapour with air, will suffice but an experienced fire investigator will be alert to the type of traces which would be left behind.

A cooker with a timer set and a pan of petrol in the oven would be obvious proof of the arsonist's work, as would any other electrical device timed to spark or produce a flame after a given interval. One device used in an episode of *New Tricks*[b] involved a condom full of petrol suspended over a candle. As the rubber melted, petrol poured out and a fire ensued. This is not as easy as it seems as a vapour/air mixture must form for ignition to occur - a cascade of falling petrol could easily extinguish the candle flame before this happens. Fire investigators are well aware of this type of device and would be alert to traces of wax and rubber at the scene.

Needless to say, placing a lighted candle in a pool of petrol, hoping it would burn down in time, would be likely to cause the rapid demise of the arsonist as the vapour catches fire.

One often-anthologised locked room short story, *The Doomdorf Mystery* by Melville Davisson Post (1914), relied on a bottle of liquid in front of a window focusing the sun's rays onto the percussion cap of an old-style shotgun, resting on a rack. The percussion cap heated up and exploded, firing the weapon and killing a man sleeping on a couch in front of it.

Apart from the stupidity of leaving a loaded shotgun sitting on a rack in a living room, this would not work since a bottle of water would not focus the sun's rays across a room in this way. It is possible to start a fire with a magnifying glass, or other lens, by focusing sunlight on flammable material but if you are planning to use this in a story, do try it out first - with a jug of water handy in case things get out of hand.

Incendiary errors

There are several clichés involving fires which appear in films and TV programmes. A common example is a character dropping a lighted cigarette into a pool of petrol which promptly catches fire. This wouldn't work as there is insufficient heat in a glowing cigarette to ignite the fuel/air mixture above the pool and the cigarette would be extinguished rapidly once it became immersed in the liquid. The creators of the website www.intuitor.com/moviephysics tested this in an exhaustive series of experiments and were unable to ignite the fuel in this way[20].

To be sure of lighting a pool of petrol you need something with a flame - a burning rag or roll of paper already soaked in the fuel would work. Throwing a "Zippo"-type lighter at the pool may also work, assuming that the flame does not go out or the lid snaps shut in transit. That would be something to test by experiment - omitting the pool of petrol, of course. This is not to say that a cigarette can never light petrol vapour but it would have to be in highly unusual circumstances, preferably in an oxygen-enriched atmosphere. But smoking while filling up the car is still not to be recommended.

The experimenters above also tried to ignite petrol with sparks produced by grinding metal above a pan of petrol. Sparks falling into the pan for several minutes failed to ignite the petrol[21]. Again, it doesn't mean that a spark can never trigger a petrol fire: it just means it's extremely unlikely.

The sequence in a British TV programme where someone made a diesel generator explode by tinkering with the wiring so it sparked was ludicrous. If you want to make diesel explode at normal temperatures you need to turn it into ANFO and use a detonator plus booster (see Chapter 4).

If sparks and cigarette ends can't ignite a petrol tank, how about bullets? Many films include scenes where someone fires a pistol or rifle at a car whereupon its fuel tank promptly explodes. This would not happen except under extreme circumstances.

Bullets are normally lead or copper-jacketed and these metals do not cause sparks. Steel does, and some bullets may contain a steel core, but even if a spark was struck inside the petrol tank it would not cause ignition - the tank would contain too little air and we have seen from the experiments de-

scribed above that sparks do not ignite petrol vapour. Bullets, although hot, are below the autoignition temperature of petrol so even if the tank was ruptured so that the fuel mixed with air and another round hit, it would not burst into flame[22].
The only reliable way of igniting a fuel tank with gunfire would be to fire a stream of incendiary bullets at it, the first few to burst the tank and the remainder to light the fuel/air mixture. This is specialist military ammunition and is not normally available to civilians, even in the U.S.

Similarly, firing into stored drums of petrol would not cause them to explode although they could burst if exposed to an external fire. The stream of hot fuel projected out through the torn drum would ignite readily when mixed with air.

It is also worth noting that most car accidents do not result in a fuel tank fire. The tank is usually protected by the rest of the car which surrounds it and even if it leaked on impact there would have to be a source of ignition. Cars do catch fire on occasions, often as a result of an electrical fault, and some cars with faulty cooling systems have been known to burst into flames[23]. An impact with another vehicle or a tumble down a cliff would not usually cause a conflagration[24].

In conclusion
I hope this chapter has provided you with some general guidance on how fires start and behave. You may be tempted to try things out at home. It's not illegal to start small fires on your own premises, provided that no damage or injury is caused and explosive materials are not used. Apart from the experiments mentioned above, I would not recommend this as a general practice - not least because it could invalidate your house insurance.

Writing fire:

- Fires are unpredictable and depend on many factors which influence the spread of flames, the rate of burning and the duration. To some extent this gives authors freedom to devise their own scenarios but they should, at least, comply with the basic laws of physics and chemistry.

- Deaths in fires are predominantly caused by smoke and toxic gas inhalation rather than heat.

- Fuels do not necessarily ignite as readily as shown on films and TV.

- A fire scene can be dangerous and pathologists, police officers and CSIs would not be allowed to enter until their safety is assured.

CHAPTER 6: FIREARMS

"*When in doubt have a man come through a door with a gun in his hand*" wrote Raymond Chandler[1] and there is no doubt that firearms play an important role in crime fiction.

Authors familiar with weapons bring credibility to their writing, although there can be a tendency to "information dump" excessive details of calibres, bullet weights and charges. Others, notably British writers, may slip up - referring to the size of a bullet as 38mm instead of .38 (of an inch), for instance, is not a mistake an American writer would make.

This chapter will set out brief descriptions of the various types of firearm, how they work, what their effects are and how some authors (screenwriters in particular) get things wrong. Some of it may seem rather basic - and if you are reading this in the U.S. you may know much of it from personal experience - but there is a reason for this. In a short, informal poll of crime writers and readers on Twitter in 2018 half the respondents (hopefully not too many writers) were unaware of the difference between a shotgun and a rifle.

What is a firearm?

Traditionally, the term has meant a device that propels a projectile by means of a controlled explosion, originally from burning gunpowder. The definition has broadened somewhat and often includes airguns, which use compressed air to propel a pellet or other missile, and weapons powered by a small cylinder of compressed gas. U.K. law defines a firearm as "a lethal barrelled weapon of any description from which any shot, bullet or other missile can be discharged" but the legislation also covers stun guns (e.g. Tasers) and devices which spray pepper extract, CS or Mace. These are prohibited except when used by the police.

Calibres

The calibre of a weapon, and the ammunition which it uses, is the diameter of the bullet (shotguns are different - see below). This may be expressed in millimetres (9mm is a common calibre) or parts of an inch (such as .303 or .38). Most countries use the metric system but the U.K. and U.S. have traditionally used Imperial measurements. Generally, the larger the calibre, the more damage a bullet can do although there are exceptions - a .357 magnum pistol cartridge packs a much greater punch than a standard .45 round as the cartridge is longer and contains more propellant.

A shotgun size is referred to as its bore (gauge in the US) which is the number of spherical lead balls fitting exactly into the barrel that together weigh a pound - thus a 16 bore shotgun barrel would accommodate a one ounce lead ball. Some smaller weapons - e.g. the .410 - use conventional measurements.

The cartridge

Apart from antique weapons - which could still fire if gunpowder can be obtained, albeit at some risk to the user - most modern small arms use cartridge ammunition. A cartridge consists of a bullet fitted into a (usually) brass cylinder, the base of which contains a primer. This is a shock-sensitive material which explodes when the cartridge is struck by the firing pin or hammer of the weapon. Centre-fire cartridges have the primer in a priming cap fitted centrally in the base of the cartridge. Rim fire cartridges have the primer distributed within the fold of the rim.

When the primer explodes it ignites the propellant in the body of the cartridge. This used to be gunpowder but the large amounts of corrosive smoke produced prompted research into smokeless powders. Cordite was used for a long time, in small arms and artillery rounds, but has now been superseded by better propellants. Propellants do not actually explode - they are low explosives and deflagrate (see Chapter 4), producing a smooth acceleration to the bullet.

Shotgun cartridges (called shells in the U.S.) are different in that they are made of plastic or compressed paper with a metal base. Instead of a bullet they contain shot - small spherical balls of metal. Wadding keeps the propellant separate from the shot, which may be contained in a plastic “cup” that falls apart when it leaves the barrel. The end of the cartridge is crimped over to keep its contents in place. Some shotgun cartridges are fitted with a solid slug of metal instead of shot. Traditionally, lead has been used for shot but tungsten and steel are used increasingly, in order to reduce lead pollution of the environment.

Gun owners, particularly in the U.S., may reload their own cartridges. Bullets, priming caps and powder are purchased separately and special tools are used to assemble the round. This enables shooters to make ammunition to their preferred specifications and avoid any possible defects in commercially manufactured rounds. This is possible in the U.K. provided that the appropriate licences are held.

Blank cartridges are simply cartridges without the bullet or shot. They are used in starting pistols and in film, TV and theatre productions. They can still be dangerous, however, as the cloud of gas and the wadding which holds the powder in place leave the muzzle at high speed and can punch their way through clothing, or flesh, at close range, the extent of the damage depending on the calibre.

Occasionally a cartridge may fail to fire immediately when the trigger of the weapon is pulled. This could be because the weapon is faulty and the primer was not struck firmly enough or because the ammunition is defective. The cartridge may be a complete dud and will never fire but sometimes the round will go off after a delay of up to a few seconds. This is called a hang fire and shooters should not eject a cartridge that fails to fire immediately - the weapon should be kept pointing at the target for at least 30 seconds before the round is ejected. A delay of two minutes is recommended in some cases[2].

Bullets

Bullets were originally made from lead, sometimes alloyed with other metals to make them harder. Given that the purpose of a fired bullet is to deliver as much damaging energy to the target as possible, lead, with its high density, is an excellent choice. Solid lead bullets, however, tend to flatten on impact and leave lead deposits in the barrel so modern ammunition is often jacketed in a harder metal such as a copper alloy. Jacketed rounds penetrate further and may fail to disable the target - they may pass right through and hit someone else standing behind.

Hollow-point and soft-point bullets have pits or apertures in the jacket which enable the softer core to expand on impact, damaging more tissue. The Hydra-Shok round takes this principle one stage further with a notched jacket and hollow point, designed to cause maximum damage on impact. Specialised ammunition designed to hit the target without passing through may also be used on aircraft. Rounds designed to expand on impact are illegal for use by civilians in the U.K. except in certain circumstances such as hunting deer, killing vermin, and the shooting of animals (e.g. escaped lions) in order to protect other animals and people. Military ammunition designed to penetrate armour, explode or ignite on impact is also prohibited for civilian use.

Rifles

Rifles are long-barrelled weapons used for hunting, military purposes and target shooting. They usually have a long range although small-bore (.22 calibre) rifles, used for target shooting and killing small animals, are only effective up to about 150 yards, depending on the weapon, as accuracy falls off at longer distances. Serious injury, however, can still be caused several hundred yards away. Specialist sniper rifles, such as the Barrett M107, are accurate to 2000 yards and the bullet may travel as far as five miles[3].

The key feature which distinguishes rifles from earlier weapons, such as muskets, is the rifling. This is a series of spiral grooves within the barrel which cause the bullet to rotate as it passes through. The bullet continues to spin on leaving the muzzle and this gives it greater stability in flight, improving accuracy. Modern pistol barrels are also rifled.

Rifles may be single shot, self-loading or automatic. Most are equipped with a magazine which holds a number of cartridges. Operating a bolt, or other mechanism such as a lever, moves a cartridge into the chamber (breech) and pulling the trigger lets a spring-loaded firing pin strike the primer, firing the round. Pulling the bolt back, or operating a lever, ejects the empty cartridge case and the process can be repeated. Some weapons do not have a magazine and each cartridge has to be loaded manually by opening the breech. They may be bolt-action or lever action.

Self-loading rifles - most military weapons are of this type - use some of the pressurised gases from the propellant to operate the reloading mechanism. In single-shot mode a fresh pull of the trigger is required to fire the weapon again but some types can be set to fire a burst or operate fully automatically after one pull (see below). Self-loading and pump action rifles, apart from the .22 rimfire calibre rifles of the type formerly used in fairground shooting galleries, are prohibited for civilian use.

Long-barrelled rifles are not the best weapon for close engagements, despite the fact that, on films and TV, you often see police storming a building with military-style rifles. They take a while to swing round to find a target and with many types of internal wall a bullet would go straight through into the next room - and possibly the room beyond that too. Shorter-barrelled weapons, called carbines, are more useful and these are used by police forces when a pistol is insufficiently powerful or accurate.

Automatic weapons

Automatic weapons continue firing once the trigger is pulled, until the magazine is empty or the pressure on the trigger is released. They range from military machine guns to hand-held submachine guns (also called machine pistols) and are illegal for private use in most countries. Some, such as the wartime Sten gun, use the recoil from the discharge to push back the breech block against a spring and eject the spent cartridge case. When the spring forces the breech block forward again it picks up another round from the magazine and the integral firing pin hits the primer when it reaches the chamber. Most automatic weapons, however, use combustion gases, diverted from the barrel, to operate the mechanism.

The rate at which a weapon fires, ejects, loads and is ready to fire again is known as the cyclic rate of fire and varies with the model of weapon. Assault rifles usually operate at 600-900 rounds per minute, sometimes higher, while submachine guns and machine pistols have cyclic rates of fire of 900-1,200 rounds per minute. These figures are misleading, however, since the weapons are never fired for a full minute continuously. If they were, the barrels would overheat and the weapon could fail - or the rounds could go off accidentally. Military machine guns require cooling and barrel changes if they are to be used for long periods. Furthermore, the typical magazine for an assault rifle or submachine gun would hold around 30 rounds. At even the lowest cyclic rate of fire mentioned above the magazine would be empty after three seconds.

It is possible to fit a semi-automatic rifle with a device called a bump stock which causes it to fire like a fully automatic weapon (see case study).

Case study: Slaughter in Las Vegas[4]

> On 1st October 2017 Stephen Paddock opened fire on a crowd of music fans at an outdoor concert in Las Vegas. He had 23 rifles in a hotel room overlooking the site, 14 of which were AR-15 types fitted with bump stocks. Over a ten minute period he fired thousands of rounds into the crowd, killing 58 people and wounding 400 more. He then shot himself.

Shotguns

Shotguns are the commonest type of firearm in British private hands, being used for game shooting, vermin control and clay pigeon shooting. They have smooth bore barrels (i.e. no rifling) and normally fire shot. As the shot leaves the barrel it spreads out forming a cloud of projectiles which makes it easier to hit a small moving target such as a bird or a clay disc. Some shotguns are fitted with a choke which reduces the spread of the shot, focusing it into a denser, tighter, pattern. This improves accuracy and range but can make it more difficult to hit a small target.

Shotguns may be single- or double-barrelled and in the latter case a separate trigger operates each barrel. Some models are fitted with a magazine holding three or more cartridges which are introduced into the chamber by means of a pump action or may operate in a semi-automatic manner. These are familiar from films and owners, who must have a good reason to own such a weapon, require a firearms certificate, with full background checks, rather than the less onerous shotgun certificate.

The sawn-off shotgun was a popular tool of armed robbers. Cutting the barrels down meant that the weapon was easier to conceal and, although lethal at close range when loaded with ordinary shot, these were generally used to frighten rather than kill. A sawn-off loaded with birdseed and fired into the ceiling of a bank created sufficient impact to persuade even the bravest clerk to hand over the money. It has long been illegal to shorten a shotgun barrel to below 24 inches in the U.K. and current legislation prohibits the possession of a firearm having a barrel less than 30cm long (see below).

Revolvers

Revolvers are handguns which feature a cylinder containing (usually) five or six chambers for the cartridges. As the hammer is pulled back (cocked), the cylinder rotates and a chamber aligns with the barrel. Pulling the trigger lets the hammer fall and strike the back of the cartridge. In a single-action revolver the hammer must be cocked manually but in a double action revolver a pull on the trigger rotates the cylinder and cocks the hammer. Cartridges are fed into the chamber either by moving the cylinder out sideways or opening the weapon so that the barrel and cylinder drops forwards. This latter design, known as top break, is largely obsolete. Quick reloading is possible using a speed loader - a clip which holds the cartridges in the same configuration as the cylinder so that they can all be dropped in simultaneously.

Revolvers are simple to operate and are unlikely to jam. They come in various calibres and barrel lengths, depending on their purpose, from pocket-sized .22 weapons with limited range and power to the .44 magnum featured in the *Dirty Harry*[a] films and the even larger Smith and Wesson Model 500 which fires a bullet half an inch in diameter. There isn't a perfect seal between the cylinder and the barrel so when a revolver is fired there is a significant escape of combustion products (gas and particles) and noise. As well as providing plenty of evidence that the shooter has fired a weapon, this means that suppressing the noise from a revolver is difficult.

Semi-automatics

Golden age crime stories frequently had the villain - or the hero - brandishing an "automatic". The term was a misnomer, however, as the pistols in question were not fully automatic but semi-automatics, in that the trigger had to be pulled for every shot.

In a semi-automatic the cartridges are held in a removable magazine (sometimes called a clip) inserted into the butt of the weapon. Before the weapon can be fired the slide has to be pulled back and released (racked). This feeds a cartridge from the magazine into the chamber and, in some models, also cocks the hammer. Pulling the trigger lets the hammer fall and fires the round. The recoil from the shot pushes the slide back, ejects the spent cartridge case, and cocks the hammer. A spring moves the slide forward which feeds a new cartridge so the weapon is ready to fire again. In some models, e.g. the Desert Eagle, gas from the burning propellant, instead of recoil, reloads the weapon but the principle is the same.

These pistols may be single action or double action. A single action weapon requires the hammer to be cocked before it can fire for the first time and this may be done manually, pulling the hammer back with a thumb, or by pulling back the slide. In a double action weapon, the first pull of the trigger cocks the hammer and then releases it. In double action/single action weapons there is the option of cocking the hammer manually or using the first, longer, trigger pull.

The magazine is easily removed from the butt and replaced with a fresh one - in some models the slide remains in the backward position, held by a catch, ready to feed a new round into the chamber when the magazine is inserted. Magazine capacities normally vary from six to 17 rounds although extensions and high capacity magazines are available for some makes. It is also common to carry the weapon with a round in the chamber ("one up the spout") as well as a full magazine, giving an extra shot. If your character disarms a shooter, they should remove the magazine and also pull back the slide to eject this extra round. In the U.K., when someone is arrested, this would normally only be done by an authorised firearms officer.

Pulling the slide back when a round is chambered will eject the unfired cartridge. A common continuity error in films and TV programmes is to have a character racking the slide in one scene, on approaching a perilous situation, and doing the same again in the next scene without a live round falling on the floor.

The mechanism of a semi-automatic pistol is more complicated than that of a revolver and there is the possibility of the weapon jamming (see case study). Semi-automatic pistols have largely replaced revolvers in law enforcement and the military since they hold more rounds and are quicker to reload. Modern weapons are more reliable than previous models and are less prone to jamming.

Case study: A royal jam[5]

In March 1974 an armed man attempted to kidnap Princess Anne by driving a van across the path of her car and forcing it to stop. Her bodyguard, Inspector Jim Beaton, got out of the car and, although shot in the shoulder, fired his semi-automatic pistol at the gunman, missing with his first shot. The pistol jammed and he could not fire again but continued to confront the would-be kidnapper. He was shot twice more and the gunman was detained by passing civilians and arriving police officers. Inspector Beaton received the George Cross for bravery.

Airguns

Airguns propel a ball bearing (BB) or pellet - usually .177 or .22 calibre - by means of compressed air. Many models are of the spring-piston design. Before the weapon is fired a spring, which drives a piston, is compressed either with a lever or by opening the gun and pushing the barrel downwards until the mechanism catches. The projectile is then loaded, the breech is closed and when the trigger is pulled the piston shoots forward, compressing the air in front of it and propelling the projectile out of the barrel. Some, low-power, air pistols have a different design but use the same principle.

Serious airgun shooters, such as Olympic competitors, use pre-charged pneumatic weapons where a reservoir is charged with compressed air, some of which is released to drive the projectile each time the trigger is pulled. The air may be compressed in the weapon by using a lever or supplied from an external cylinder such as those used by divers. This type of airgun has much less recoil than the spring type and is therefore more accurate. A further type uses a carbon dioxide gas bulb, of the sort used in soda syphons, as the source of energy.

An unusual design was the Brocock range of revolvers which used self-contained gas cartridges. These resembled normal cartridges on the outside but were pumped up individually and the projectile was loaded on the front. These are now prohibited in the U.K., although existing owners were allowed to retain them if they held a firearms certificate, because the revolvers were easily converted by criminals to fire conventional ammunition[6]. They are still available in other countries.

The power of airguns can sometimes be increased by "dieseling". Here, a small amount of oil is placed behind the pellet and the rapid compression as the piston moves forward briefly increases the air temperature in the barrel and causes the oil to burn or explode (in the same way that diesel engines work), giving added impetus to the pellet. This sometimes occurs when excessive lubricant is used in the weapon and there is some dispute among airgunners as to how significant this phenomenon is. Dieseling an airgun could take it over the U.K. power limits and render it illegal.

Airguns are not regulated in the same way as other weapons, because of their lower power. In the U.K., below a certain power level they are exempt from licensing (although there are restrictions on who may possess them and where) but above these limits a firearms certificate is required. Although unregulated air weapons are rarely lethal, it was estimated some years ago that one person dies per year in the U.K. from airgun injuries[7]. Unsurprisingly, children are the most vulnerable. In July 2018 a six-year old boy in Yorkshire, U.K., died after being accidentally shot in the abdomen by his great grandfather who was subsequently convicted of manslaughter (second degree murder in the U.S). Press reports suggested that the weapon in question was above the U.K. power limit as the shooter was also convicted of possessing it without a firearms certificate[8]. Some air weapons can be much more powerful and may rival small-bore firearms in impact. A high-powered airgun featured in the Sherlock Holmes story *The Empty House* (1905).

Air cane

An unusual, old airgun, is the air cane, a weapon which resembles a walking stick. The device is first pumped up and the compressed air is stored in a small reservoir. A projectile is loaded from the muzzle and when the trigger is pulled it is propelled out at great speed. Air canes cannot be used in the U.K. (weapons which resemble something else are banned and, anyway, they are more powerful than permitted air rifles) but can be collected as curios. An air cane was the probable cause of an unsolved murder described in *The Other Mr Churchill*, a biography of the pioneering forensic gun expert[9].

From a murderer's point of view, air weapons have limited use. To kill someone you would need to be very accurate and fire from a short range. They are, however, quiet. Given that pellets from legal air pistols can penetrate the skin, an air weapon could be used to deliver poison or an allergen, provided that your killer could get hold of something sufficiently toxic. Reginald Hill, in *A Clubbable Woman* (1970), had someone killed by an (unloaded) air pistol but this was a type where the whole barrel shoots forward with its back end compressing the air to fire the pellet. The impact of the barrel caused a skull injury which proved fatal. While the author kept us guessing as to exactly how the victim was killed, the publisher gave it away by including a photograph of the pistol on the cover of one paperback edition.

Dart guns

Dart guns are weapons designed to fire a dart containing a drug for tranquillising an animal which cannot otherwise be sedated. Dart guns are otherwise prohibited and a firearms certificate is required to possess them. The simplest version is a lung-powered blowpipe but this is only effective up to 10-15 metres. More sophisticated dart pistols and rifles use carbon dioxide cylinders or an integral reservoir for air which is pressurised using a pump. Other versions use a .22 blank cartridge as the energy source. The darts contain drugs which are injected via a syringe on impact, either by a small explosive charge or compressed air[10]. In some cases the momentum of a steel ball behind the plunger of the syringe is sufficient to inject the drug. A wide range of drugs can be used depending on the type and size of animal to be tranquillised and the depth of effect required. Given that such animals are nearly always larger than humans, using one of these on a person is likely to prove fatal (see also Chapter 3).

Starting pistols

Starting pistols are blank-firing devices used to start races and, sometimes, to train dogs. Designs vary but they are not capable of firing live ammunition when manufactured - in some designs the flash and noise emerges from the top of the weapon rather than from the dummy barrel. Some types can be converted to fire live ammunition, however, and in 2010 the Olympic .38 BBM was banned in the U.K. because it was easily converted into a live-firing realistic pistol. Several people have been convicted of offences in connection with converted Olympic .38 BBMs, including one for attempted murder[11].

Plastic pistols

With the appropriate 3-D printer and software it is now possible to make a plastic pistol, which would bypass airport security scanners, in the privacy of your own home. Such a weapon would be untraceable. The digital files are freely available on the internet and thousands of copies have been downloaded worldwide[12].

These weapons are illegal in most countries although they are permitted in the U.S. provided that a non-removable metal part is included to ensure metal detectors can find the gun. Current printers use the plastic ABS which is not strong enough for repeated use - when the Australian police produced a number of these weapons using a desktop printer they all blew up when fired[13]. A 3-D printer using metal would create a more viable weapon but, as these are extremely expensive, it would probably be easier for your character to acquire a weapon by other means. Such printers may become cheaper in the future.

In March 2019 a student at Southbank University, London, U.K. faced a number of firearms charges relating to the alleged manufacture of two handguns using composite materials and a 3D printer[14].

Reactivated weapons
It is legal to possess certain types of weapons without a firearms certificate provided that they have been deactivated - i.e. they cannot be fired. In many instances, however, it is possible for a reasonably skilled gunsmith to reactivate such a weapon to fire as originally intended. This is quite a profitable trade for underworld armourers (see below), some of whom, at the time of writing, are serving time[15].

Flying lead
A flying bullet is subject to gravity, just like anything else, so it will never travel in a straight, horizontal line. It will drop as it flies and the longer it is in flight the more it will drop. The sights on a rifle compensate for this so the barrel is pointed slightly upwards, allowing for this drop, and the path of the bullet is, technically, a parabola. At short ranges the drop is small but is much more significant for snipers operating at long ranges. The bullets from long range weapons travel extremely fast which helps to minimise drop. Zoe Sharp's *Dancing on the Grave* (2018) describes the use of a Barrett sniper rifle which fires a bullet at nearly three times the speed of sound. This means that the bullet arrives seconds before the shot is heard.

Gravity is not the only influence on a long-range shot.
Wind can deflect a bullet so this must be allowed for and even atmospheric humidity can have an effect. Lee Child's One *Shot* (2015) describes (spoiler alert) how a sniper may fire the first shot to establish exactly where the round is going while the

second shot is the one designed to hit the real target.
The accuracy of a weapon also depends on its barrel length - short-barrelled revolvers, for instance, are only really accurate at a few feet. For the same cartridge, the power and range also increase with barrel length as the expanding gases have more time to accelerate the bullet.

A further factor is recoil. Basic physics means that if you have a fast-moving bullet leaving a weapon in one direction there will be an equal force exerted on the weapon in the opposite direction. This is the recoil or "kick" and, particularly in inexperienced shooters, can affect the trajectory of the bullet. It can also be painful - anyone firing a .44 magnum revolver incautiously is likely to break their wrist while shoulder protection is needed for heavy calibre rifles. There is also a tendency for the muzzle to rise as a weapon is fired and some have a modification to the barrel end, called a muzzle brake, which compensates for this.

Putting these factors together you can see why the scene in a TV thriller, where someone who had never fired a gun before picks up a revolver with a short barrel and shoots someone fifteen feet away in the head, without hitting either the hostage they were holding, the ceiling or the wall behind, is beyond silly.

Range
There are two aspects to the range of a weapon: how far the bullet will travel and still do damage and the distance at which the shooter can reasonably be expected to hit the target.
"Ordinary" rifles are accurate to several hundred yards, in the hands of a skilled shooter, and sniper rifles to much greater distances (see above). The maximum range, at which the bullet can still be lethal or do serious damage, is much longer.
For instance, the U.S. M16 rifle is reported to be effective at 550 metres but still dangerous at 3,600[16].

For the purposes of most crime novels, pistol ranges are more useful since handguns feature more than rifles. A skilled shooter with a well-maintained weapon and special sights, under perfect conditions, can use a 9mm pistol accurately up to 100 metres, although the bullet will still be dangerous beyond half a mile. For a new shooter the effective range is likely to be 7-10 metres[17]. Under combat conditions, under fire and with no time to line up a shot precisely, the distance is much shorter. Lee Child, in *Personal* (2015), quotes the F.B.I.'s statistics to the effect that the average distance for "a successful handgun engagement" is 11 feet.

Accuracy is not important for automatic weapons since their purpose is to spray the target area with bullets in the hope that some may hit the target. Indeed, some small automatic weapons are referred to as "spray and pray" because they are so hard to control and aim at a specific target. The MAC-10 is a prime example, firing 20 rounds per second with no hope of carefully aimed fire. This weapon has been used by gangs in Birmingham (U.K.) and elsewhere[18] and although it may be inaccurate it does terrify those on the receiving end. The scenes on TV and films where someone fires such a weapon and a perfectly straight line of bullet holes appears across the wall is the stuff of fantasy.

Penetration
A high velocity bullet is difficult to stop and wooden walls, plasterboard or upturned tables are unlikely to do the job. Large calibre weapons, such as sniper rifles, can even penetrate brickwork although the path of the bullet once it reaches the other side is unpredictable. Pistol rounds can easily penetrate plasterboard and some can also travel a considerable distance through wood[19] so hiding behind a door is unlikely to protect a potential victim unless the weapon involved is a low-powered, small calibre model.

Realistic imitation firearms
Many people like to collect imitation firearms and these are widely available without the need for a licence provided that they are easily distinguishable from a real firearm e.g. by colour. Realistic imitations are permitted for certain purposes - acting props and airsoft skirmishing, for instance - but someone using a realistic imitation weapon for criminal purposes would be treated as if they were using a real firearm and possibly shot. Some air pistols are accurate replicas of real firearms and it would be entirely understandable if an authorised fire-

arms officer shoots somebody carrying one in the belief that it is real. It is illegal, in the U.K., to carry such weapons in a public place.

Getting shot

In film and TV land, getting shot usually involves falling down and dying almost immediately, perhaps squeezing off a final shot in return or uttering memorable last words. In reality it isn't like that. Unless someone is hit in the head, heart or the top of the spinal column death takes considerably longer and normally results from bleeding or an inability to breathe.

The damage done by a bullet depends on its mass, velocity and what happens to it once it hits the body. All bullets wreck the tissues they hit and cause a cavity - a space is left along the bullet track where tissue has been damaged. High velocity bullets cause a pressure wave which produces a much larger, albeit temporary, cavity, causing considerably more damage[20]. Such rounds may also tumble or yaw (wobble) as they decelerate, wreaking more havoc on the body. Unless they hit a bone and either stop dead or bounce around inside the body until their energy is dissipated, higher velocity rounds will tend to pass straight through the body. This is why some pistol rounds are made to expand on impact, causing much more damage and increasing the chances of hitting a vital structure. It also reduces the chances of someone standing behind the target being wounded. Similarly, bullets which fragment can do much more widespread damage than those which retain their structure.

A gunshot wound to the head is not necessarily fatal. If a small round passes through non-vital areas and out the other side the victim may survive[21] but if it bounces around inside the skull the prognosis is poor. A direct hit to the top of the spinal column is likely to kill, quickly, as all systems controlled by the brain shut down. Lower down, spinal damage is likely to lead to paralysis of various functions depending on the exact position.

A shot to the heart is likely to prove rapidly fatal as tissues are deprived of oxygen when the heart stops. Similarly, if a major blood vessel or the spleen is ruptured the victim is likely to bleed out, the time taken depending on what is hit. Someone hit in the femoral artery, for instance, is likely to bleed out in a few minutes. Damage to other organs, such as the liver and kidneys, may be survivable depending on its extent but a ruptured bowel spilling its contents into the abdominal cavity is likely to cause peritonitis which is extremely unpleasant. A bullet through the lung may cause it to fill up with blood and cease to function while a hole in the chest cavity can prevent the lungs from inflating (pneumothorax). An accumulation of blood in the chest can also prevent the heart from beating effectively (cardiac tamponade).

So, as far as fatal injuries are concerned, the result is a combination of physics, biology and luck. Longer term effects, however, are often misrepresented, both on screen and in print. Apart from the psychological trauma of being wounded, physical effects can be long term, especially when damage to the nervous system is involved. Permanent nerve damage may be caused by a bullet as nerves cannot easily repair themselves. Bones, too, can take a long time to heal. Someone shot in the shoulder is unlikely to return to work three days later with just their arm in a sling and a rueful grin. The chances of your hero using the arm for anything useful at all in the near future, let alone shooting villains, driving, carrying out raids or making an arrest, are slight.

The discussion so far has focused on wounds from bullets fired from rifles and handguns. Shotgun wounds are different. A blast from a shotgun contains a lot of energy but as the shot spreads out this is dissipated. At close range it is devastating, punching a large hole through tissues which is likely to prove rapidly fatal if the head or chest is hit. The exact potential for damage depends on the bore of the weapon and the type of shot used but shotguns can be lethal up to as much as 40 metres[22]. Some shotgun and cartridge combinations are dangerous, although not fatal, at up to 450 yards[23]. At longer ranges the pellets are more spread out and each one carries a relatively small amount of energy, unless it is a large type such as buckshot, so damage is less. Painful injuries are still likely to result when the pellets penetrate the skin including the condition known as “poacher’s bottom”, the cause of which can be readily imagined.

Forensic aspects

It is well known that bullets can be matched to the weapon that fired them although it is not always as clear as is sometimes thought[24]. The lands (raised sections) in the barrel of a rifled weapon leave marks on the bullet as it passes through and they can narrow down the possible make involved. Provided that the bullet isn’t too badly damaged a comparison microscope can be used to match a bullet to one fired from a specific weapon.

A spent cartridge case will bear identifying marks from the hammer or firing pin, from the breech, from the extractor (the claw which pulls out the spent case in an automatic or semi-automatic weapon) and any other part of the weapon which it strikes. Corresponding marks can be found on the brass base of a shotgun cartridge. If the shooter has reloaded the cartridges at home, marks from the tools used can be characteristic - this aspect featured in Isabelle Grey’s *Shot Through the Heart* (2016) where the key to the case was the ammunition rather than the rifle.

Chemistry plays its part in identifying nefarious firearms use. Anyone firing a weapon is likely to have traces of burnt or partially burnt powder on their clothes or skin, especially if the weapon is a revolver which blasts gases out sideways or a semi-automatic pistol which releases gases as the spent cartridge case is ejected. Swabbing anyone known to be at the crime scene is routine. The explosives in the shock-sensitive primers used in cartridge cases can be indicative as well since they contain varying proportions of metals, such as copper, lead and barium depending on the brand. Traces can sometimes be found: by examining curtains, investigators were able to identify which window weapons had been fired from following the shooting of WPC Yvonne Fletcher outside the Libyan embassy in 1984[25].

Not-so-silent killers

A mythical creation in many crime novels and screenplays is the almost-silent firearm. A quiet “phut” or two and the victim

hits the floor, making more noise as he or she falls than the weapon which put them there. With a few exceptions, firearms are not that quiet.
The noise from a firearm comes from several different sources: the expanding gases from the burning propellant, mechanical noise from the mechanism as it loads, fires and ejects the spent case (if it is automatic or semi-automatic) and, importantly, the sonic crack of a bullet breaking the sound barrier. These can be mitigated in three main ways.

The most common method is to fit a suppressor (incorrectly referred to as a silencer). This tube, which fits on the end of the barrel, allows the gases to expand and may also contain sound absorbing material, thereby reducing one source of sound. Slowing the bullet down to less than the speed of sound is crucial - some suppressors may do this but the most effective way is to load the cartridge with less powder, (see below) or buy subsonic ammunition, so the bullet never reaches the critical velocity.

A third approach is to use a manually loaded single-shot weapon which will create less mechanical noise if used carefully as there will be fewer moving parts to rub against each other and no automatic ejection of the case.
Simply fitting a suppressor will help - there are demonstrations on the internet - but may not do enough. It will merely reduce the sound to a quieter crack. A suppressor on a revolver is likely to be ineffective as sound escapes between the cylinder and the barrel, along with gases and flame.

A three-inch long suppressor (as seen in some films) is likely to be barely useful, as is one fitted to a submachine gun. Suppressors can be fitted to other weapons - you can buy one for a Barrett sniper rifle which cuts the sound somewhat and reduces muzzle flash[26], making it more difficult to spot the sniper's position, - but in many jurisdictions suppressors are illegal.

So, if your character is looking to shoot someone quietly, what are the options? The best bet is the Welrod, a very quiet pistol using subsonic ammunition developed for special forces in the Second World War[27]. Fire this against someone's back or chest and the shot would not be heard in the next room. Kate Atkinson had a character use one in *One Good Turn* (2007). The bad news, from the writer's point of view, is that these are no longer manufactured and are not widely available although there may still be a few war souvenirs around.

There are modern very quiet pistols, such as the B&T VP9 which is based on the Welrod. This is said to make about as much noise as a car door closing[28].

With some skill and equipment the shooter could cut down the powder in a normal cartridge, although the range and penetration (i.e. killing power) is reduced. A semi-automatic pistol may not reload as reliably with a reduced charge in the cartridge. A smaller calibre weapon is usually quieter than a larger sized one but the same reduction in lethality applies.

Air weapons - including the air cane mentioned above - are a possibility but the killer would either have to obtain one more powerful than those generally available in the U.K. or be extraordinarily lucky with a shot.

One final weapon worth mentioning is the MB Gyrojet pistol which fired small rockets. This was discontinued decades ago but there may still be a few around in the U.S. - although obtaining viable ammunition would be very difficult. A click and a hiss was all the sound this made - but it is, perhaps, only of use if your story is set in America during the 1960s.

Before leaving the topic of noise it is important to remember the fact that gunshots can be very loud. Police officers - and gun fans - practising on the range wear ear protection for a reason and a firefight indoors is likely to leave participants and spectators with tinnitus. The actor Linda Hamilton's hearing was permanently damaged during shooting the film *Terminator 2*[b] when she omitted to put in earplugs for a scene where she fired a gun in a lift[29] - and this would have been firing blanks and quieter than normal weapons.

Getting a gun

In the U.K. it is reasonably easy to obtain a shotgun for clay pigeon or animal shooting. A certificate is needed from the police who will want to ensure you are a fit and proper person (U.K. ex-prisoners are, generally, not allowed to hold firearms) and that you can store the weapon securely. Similarly, you can purchase and keep a rifle if you have good reason to own one but a firearms certificate, involving more stringent background checks, is required. Handguns, (in fact any firearm with a barrel less than 30cm long) are no longer permitted in private hands since legislation was enacted in the aftermath of the Dunblane tragedy, when a deranged individual used legally held pistols to shoot pupils and staff at a Scottish primary school[30]. Even before this you needed a very good reason to own a pistol - self-defence was not one of them.

So, how will your character get hold of a firearm if needed? Professional criminals have access to underworld armourers who can supply, often on loan, a weapon for a price. If it is returned unfired the hire charge is less than if it has been used, having possibly left evidence to link it to a crime. In some cases, getting the weapon is relatively easy but obtaining ammunition is more difficult - armourers may not wish to supply it and you cannot buy it without a firearms certificate.

Illegal firearms may be smuggled into the country by criminals[31] or brought home as souvenirs by soldiers serving in war zones. In an ITV documentary broadcast in 2018, Ross Kemp interviewed an anonymous gun dealer who claimed to import 50-100 unused handguns into the U.K. per week, mainly from the U.S. via west coast ports. The going rate for a Beretta 9mm semi-automatic pistol plus 50 rounds of ammunition was £4-5,000, the purchasers being mainly drug dealers who needed protection[32].

Weapons from underworld armourers may be conventional guns, reactivated legally held deactivated weapons or starting pistols and replicas converted to fire live ammunition - not always a safe practice. In some cases they may be made from scratch - in August 2018 an illegal arms factory in Sussex (U.K.) was discovered with handguns, machinery and blueprints found on the premises[33]. Increasingly, "clean" (unused) weapons are being imported so the "rented out" model is becoming less popular while some weapons are smuggled in as component parts hidden in other packages[34]. Shotguns make up 40% of illegally used firearms (in the U.K.) and these are often stolen in burglaries[35].

Case study: *Zorakis*[36]

> *Zorakis* are Turkish-made blank-firing pistols which can operate as semi-automatic or fully automatic weapons. They are easily convertible to handle live ammunition and can fire eight rounds per second. In 2017, Matthew Harwozinski bought dozens of *Zorakis* from a Czech arms dealer and imported them into the U.K. whereupon Ricky Garner converted them to handle live ammunition in his shed in Bedford. The converted weapons, by then worth up to £2000 each, were supplied to criminals and used in a number of shootings around the country. Some, but not all, were recovered by the police and both men are now serving life sentences. *Zorakis* are illegal in the U.K.

The ordinary person wanting a firearm, especially a handgun, would find one much more difficult to obtain than a working criminal would. Many stories feature a relative's "old service revolver" (presumably illegally retained on leaving the army) or a Luger pistol captured from a German officer in the First or Second World War. Many such souvenirs were handed in during an amnesty following the Dunblane massacre but a few will still be held illegally. Provided that the weapon has been kept dry and oiled it may well work perfectly well and the ammunition may still fire. Corroded cartridges may fail to work, however, and a rusted weapon may either not fire or disintegrate - see Paul Finch's *The Killing Club* (2014) for a dramatic example.

If you are planning a story set in the past it is worth checking what legislation was in force at the time.

Currently, the Firearms Act 1968 is the basis for control in the U.K. but it has been amended on a number of occasions since its enactment. Prior to that there were other controls on various types of weapon. For current measures the Home Office Guide on Firearms Licensing Law[37] provides detailed information on the controls on all types of firearm from airguns to rocket launchers (spoiler: you can't have one of those). Proposals to ban the possession of long-range sniper rifles were blocked by a group of Conservative MPs during the debate over Brexit in 2018[38].

Case study: Armed paedophile[39] (USA = pedophile)

> In March 2019 George Crossland, from Harrogate (U.K.), was jailed for possessing over two million indecent images of children and a range of illegally held firearms and ammunition. Among his illegal weapons were several conventional semi-automatic pistols and three Brocock-type revolvers. He held much more ammunition than his firearms certificate permitted and some of this was pistol ammunition designed to expand on impact - also illegal. Crossland kept his weapons, and pornography, in an underground bunker complex and shooting range constructed from shipping containers. He had been a long-standing member of shooting clubs and had, presumably, acquired the weapons over a number of years.

Hollywood howlers

I have already pointed out a number of mistakes which writers and film producers make but there are several more worth mentioning. The first violates a fundamental principle of physics, the law of conservation of momentum, and we've all seen it happen on films: the shooter fires a shotgun or other weapon at the victim who is then blown off their feet and across the room, often through a door or window.

Given that the shot or bullet does not magically acquire energy in flight, the momentum of the shot plus victim would be the same as the momentum of the shooter plus weapon, although in the opposite direction. In short, if the target is blown across the room x feet, the shooter should be blown x feet backwards, which never happens - Ross Armstrong explained this correctly in *Head Case* (2018).

Being hit by a shotgun blast at close range would certainly knock you down but not into the air! As to being blown through a window, glass and joinery are much stronger than they appear to be in Hollywood - but that's another story. Offences against the laws of physics are discussed further in Tom Rogers' excellent book Insultingly *Stupid Movie Physics*[40]. Windows feature in another common error - the shot through glass. A bullet travelling through glass will inevitably be deflected as the window breaks and fragments fly off in all directions. To be sure of hitting the target the shooter would have to fire once to break the window and again to score a hit - assuming that the target hasn't moved. An automatic weapon would fire quickly enough but it would be difficult to maintain accuracy, particularly at any distance.

The scene in a popular television series where the hero shot someone 20 or 30 feet away, through two windows, with a handgun was completely ridiculous.

Many windows are made of toughened or laminated glass which can resist penetration by a bullet - although they won't stop every type of round. A toughened vehicle windscreen may not be penetrated by a pistol round and, even if it was, the trajectory of the bullet in the vehicle would be unpredictable. Following the 2017 terrorist attack in Westminster (U.K.), when a car mowed down numerous pedestrians, counter-terrorist police officers have been issued with high-powered rifle ammunition capable of penetrating armoured glass and body armour[41] so that the driver of a lorry or other vehicle used as a weapon can be stopped.

Shooting out a lock with a pistol is a common means of escape in films but this is generally a bad idea. A bullet fired at a steel lock, e.g. on a barred cell door, is likely to bounce straight off and possibly stop any escape plan dramatically. As lead, and copper jacketing, is softer than steel the bullet is likely to make little impression on the lock anyway. You could shoot a series of holes around the lock area in a wooden door so that it is weakened but that would waste a lot of ammunition and warn anyone within earshot of your plans. Firing into the lock itself would wreck the mechanism, possibly jamming it completely.

The infinite magazine is another Hollywood cliché which, it must be admitted, some producers are addressing by providing characters with replacement magazines for their weapons. Automatic rifles generally have a magazine holding about 30 rounds and at a rate of fire of 600 rounds per minute it would be empty in three seconds. In many films they keep firing for much longer - in *Lock, Stock and Two Smoking Barrels*[c] a character manages to get several hundred rounds out of a 28-round Bren gun magazine without reloading. Furthermore, in films the barrels of automatic weapons never get too hot to handle after prolonged firing, unlike in real life.
In fairness, crime writers do not usually make this mistake but it is always worth keeping a tally of rounds fired before the character reloads.

Safety catches
Many writers have their protagonists switching off the safety catch of their pistols before using them. In the case of most semi-automatics this is perfectly correct – a small lever or button has to be manipulated before the weapon can fire. Revolvers, however, do not usually have safety catches (some old models might) and Glock semi-automatics do not either. In the case of the Glock a small lever on the trigger acts as a safety feature – if the trigger is not pulled correctly so that the lever is compressed the gun will not fire.

Writing firearms

- Be clear about the different types of firearm and ammuni tion used by your protagonist.

- Note the limitations of range and, particularly, accuracy `applying to different types of weapon.

- If someone is shot they will rarely die immediately unless hit in the head, heart or upper spinal column.

- Suppressors have a limited effect, especially on revolvers.

- For the average person, getting hold of a handgun is very difficult.

- There is a thriving trade in smuggled, converted or reactivated weapons which supplies professional crimi nals.

- Someone picking up a handgun in the U.K., or using it occasionally for criminal purposes, will never have the skill acquired by someone who spends most weekends at a shooting range.

CHAPTER 7: WEAPONS AND TACTICS

This chapter will look at other potential weapons and means of murder which have been used in real life and fiction and look at some popular escape scenarios, pointing out a few improbabilities and suggesting solutions.
It will not cover novel or undetectable ways of killing people or set out new ways of covering up a crime.

Part 1: Means of murder

Electricity

Electricity can be dangerous. Half the accidental fires in homes in England during the year 2017/18 were caused by electrical faults[1], and in a typical year around 20 people die from electricity related fires[2]. Deaths from electric shock are rare in the U.K. - only 13 occurred in 2017, a figure which includes workplace deaths but not those related to transmission lines[3]. Despite this, killing someone with electricity does make an appearance in fiction, notably by dropping an electrical appliance into the bath as in the film *Goldfinger*[a]. But how realistic is it? The short answer is that it depends on the specific circumstances.

Most British homes are fitted with very sensitive circuit breakers (residual current or earth leakage detectors) which shut off the power if too much current flows in the wrong place. This is meant to ensure that someone touching live equipment does not receive a fatal shock. Other countries and older buildings may not have such sophisticated protection - or the wiring regulations which require it - and the risks are correspondingly greater so these are points worth checking if you are setting a story outside the U.K. or in the past.

Electricity will flow to earth by the path of least resistance. If you are holding a live wire and standing in a full bath with metal drainage fittings the path of least resistance is you and current will flow. If you touch that wire standing on a polypropylene carpet in rubber boots, there will be a much greater resistance and little current will flow (it is still not to be recommended). Dropping an appliance into the bath is not necessarily fatal[4] - unless you are holding it, the current will flow through the water rather than you, as it is a better conductor, and the power will shut off. If you are holding a wet appliance and sitting in the bath the result could be very different.

Case study: Fatal bath[5]

> In 2016 a London man died in the bath while charging his *iPhone* using an extension lead plugged into a socket outside the room. He rested the charger on his chest, but the lead and socket connected to the mains became wet and the current flowing through his body killed him. Contrary to the comments of the coroner, this was not a problem with the phone.

Similar incidents have occurred elsewhere - it is not the low voltage flowing to the phone from the charger that is dangerous but the high voltage carried by the lead connected to the mains.

Air embolism

Injecting air into the circulatory system to cause a fatal embolism is a well-known plot device and a means of murder in real life. Air, or gas, embolisms can form accidentally during scuba diving and some surgical procedures. A bubble of air in a vein is not as serious as one in an artery, which could prevent blood reaching organs thus depriving them of oxygen. In the case of the heart this could cause a heart attack and if an embolism reaches the brain it can cause a stroke and death - just 2-3ml of air in the brain can be fatal[6].

In 2018 a Texas nurse, William George Davis, was charged with murdering two people and leaving two others in a vegetative state by injecting them with air[7]. One of Beverley Allitt's victims (see Chapter 2) was also found to have a large air bubble in the circulation.

Murder by air embolism is not undetectable - Noburo Kato, who was murdered by his girlfriend in Tokyo, was found to have air in the right side of his heart rather than blood, indicating that at least 50ml had been injected[10]. There will be a puncture mark if a direct injection is given although Davis was accused of injecting air into his victims' IV lines, which would not leave a trace. A large embolism might well be detected at a post mortem but if one causes a stroke or heart attack in someone already prone to such illnesses, it might go unnoticed. If the victim has been seen by a doctor recently a post mortem may not be carried out unless there is a suspicion of foul play.

Case study: Deadly deacon[8]

> In January 2018 Ivo Poppe, a Belgian nurse who became a Catholic Deacon, was charged with killing at least 10 people by injecting them with air and was later convicted of five murders including those of his mother and father. He had previously admitted to his psychiatrist that he had killed up to 20 people[9]. Poppe was jailed for 27 years.

Crossbows

Crossbows as murder weapons have featured in a number of stories, notable M.J.Arlidge's *Down to the Woods* (2018). They are quiet, accurate and can be extremely powerful - a *YouTube* demonstration shows one firing a bolt through lightweight body armour normally capable of stopping most pistol bullets[11]. The damage caused by a crossbow bolt, and its range, depend on the draw weight - how much force is needed to pull back the string. In the video mentioned above the draw weight was 200lbs, which is quite high, but weapons requiring a lower draw weight can still be lethal.

Hunting websites discuss shooting deer and other animals with crossbows, pointing out that they do not have the range of a firearm but are effective at shorter distances. A full-sized, powerful crossbow could be lethal to a human at many tens of yards. In most cases the bolt would kill by severing major blood vessels and causing a severe haemorrhage. If it hit the heart or penetrated the skull and brain (not impossible at close range) death would be much quicker. Even a smaller pistol crossbow can be lethal at close range with a lucky - or unlucky, depending on your perspective - shot.

Crossbows have been used in murders. In 2018 a Humberside man was killed with a crossbow and his alleged assailant, a neighbour, was later found dead in his car[12] whilst in June of that year a Missouri resident was convicted of killing his father with a crossbow and hiding the body in a freezer[13].

In Canada in 2017, Brett Ryan stabbed his mother with a crossbow bolt (a dangerous weapon in its own right) and strangled her then shot one of his brothers in the head with a crossbow, stabbing another brother with a bolt[14].

In May 2019 a 74 year old man in Anglesey, North Wales died after being struck by a crossbow bolt which passed through his upper body and arm. At the time of writing the circumstances of the injury are unclear[15].

Despite their potential lethality, there are few controls on crossbows in the U.K. Anyone over 18 can purchase one and no licence is needed. It is illegal to hunt animals with a crossbow (or longbow) and carrying one in public would be construed as possessing an offensive weapon - they can only be used on private land.
Some skill is needed to fire one accurately, and a modicum of strength is needed to cock a powerful device, but with something this quiet your character could practise for hours without disturbing the neighbours.

Knives
Knives are one of the commonest causes of death by homicide in fact and in fiction. According to leading pathologist Dr Richard Shepherd, "The knife in every kitchen drawer in the land is a murder waiting to happen"[16]. They are readily available and easily concealed although carrying one in public in the U.K. without a good reason is an imprisonable offence

Statistics[17]

> In the year ending March 2017 36% of the homicides recorded in England and Wales were by knives or other sharp implements. The deaths at Hillsborough (see p161) have been excluded since they took place previously but were only recorded as homicides during that year. Between 2015/16 and 2017/8 the number of life-threatening stab wounds treated by nine of the 11 NHS major trauma centres in England increased by 34.2%[18].

Death from stabbing usually occurs through loss of blood, although a stab wound to the brain could be fatal and the heart can be stopped quickly (after about 12 seconds) if penetrated by a blade. If blood builds up around the heart as a result of a severed blood vessel in the chest the pressure can stop the heart from beating, a condition called cardiac tamponade. Stab wounds are rarely instantly fatal as it takes time for sufficient blood to escape and deprive vital organs of oxygen. Someone may not realise that they have been fatally stabbed - Susie Steiner provides a graphic and credible account of this in *Persons Unknown* (2018) - and can appear relatively uninjured before collapsing[19].

Even if a major organ is not penetrated by a blade, stabbing can easily be fatal. The body is networked with major blood vessels and cutting any one of them could lead to a life-threatening haemorrhage. Arteries, which carry blood away from the heart to the rest of the body, contain blood at high pressure moving in a pulsating manner.

Cutting an artery, e.g. one of the carotid arteries in the neck, can cause blood to spray a considerable distance. The flow of blood through veins, which return blood to the heart, is smoother and at a lower pressure. A wound to a vein can still be fatal though - cutting the jugular, also in the neck, would lead to death fairly rapidly and suicides who slash their wrists usually cut veins rather than the (deeper) arteries. Some authors have confused the two groups of vessels in the neck - there is no pulsing arterial spray from a severed jugular, just a large but steadier blood flow.

Some gang fights appear to involve stabbings which are intended to wound but not kill. This rarely works.
Dr Ross Davenport, consultant in trauma and vascular surgery at the Royal London Hospital, told the *Guardian*

> *"Life-changing and fatal injuries are possible from a wound anywhere - it is a complete myth there is a safe place to stab someone[20]".*

If you are thinking of having a character stab themselves "safely" to throw the police off the scent, bear this in mind (and the same goes for characters shooting themselves in a limb - it won't end well).

Remember, also, that you do not need a long blade to inflict a fatal injury. A utility knife blade is long enough to sever a carotid artery and a small penknife could reach the femoral artery in the thigh if sharp enough.

In the U.K., possession of a knife or other "bladed article" in a public place without good reason is an offence and some types of knife, e.g. flick knives (switchblades), are illegal - there is no lawful excuse for having one in the street or anywhere else and the same goes for swordsticks. Illegal knives are often found and confiscated by the Border Force from people returning from abroad.

Blunt instruments
Beating someone to death with a blunt instrument, be it a golf club, block of wood, a baseball bat or a boot, is a common scenario in both fiction and real life. The most vulnerable area is the head but fatal injuries can also be incurred from blows elsewhere on the body. A sharp blow above the heart can stop it, a ruptured spleen can lead to a fatal haemorrhage if not treated and a broken rib can be driven into a vital organ if repeatedly struck. In many real life cases, a series of blows is delivered in a frenzied attack but one blow to the head with something sufficiently hard and fast moving can cave in the skull and cause fatal brain damage. A lighter blow may cause a haematoma

which does not prove fatal until sometime later (see also Chapter 3).

Fistfights as depicted on screen are frequently highly unrealistic - the repeated blows to the head and face from bare knuckles would undoubtedly cause severe, and probably fatal, trauma, to say nothing of knocked-out teeth and the damage done to the fighters' fists. One punch can be lethal and there have been several tragic cases reported in the media where a single blow during an altercation has led to someone's death.

In 2017 a 16 year old boy accidentally killed a man in Blackpool (U.K.) with one punch when showing off[21] while in 2018 a man from Northern Ireland killed a member of the traveller community with one blow although in the latter case the victim struck his head on the pavement when he fell. Both assailants were convicted of manslaughter (roughly equivalent to second degree murder in the U.S.)[22]. Very rarely, a single blow to the chest can cause fatal damage to the heart but this is more likely to happen by accident than design[23].

Another film and TV mistake is the effect of a blow on the head with a bottle. Bar-room fights always involve someone having a bottle smashed over their head and a shower of glass flying around. In many cases, the skull is likely to be damaged more than the bottle which will rarely break in this manner. Bottles used as props are made from sugar, or another readily frangible material, and smash without causing a haematoma or depressed skull fracture.

This is not the place for a detailed discussion of autopsies but it is worth mentioning that a pathologist will rarely say that a particular object definitely caused a specific injury simply by looking at the shape of the damage. Unless there is other evidence, such as DNA on the item in question, an expert witness will only say that the object could have caused the injuries rather than that it certainly did[24].

Give us a brake

A common ploy in crime fiction is to cut the brake pipes of a car so that it cannot be stopped, with potentially fatal results for the driver. In some circumstances this may work but there are other ways of slowing down a car without using the foot brake. A clear-headed driver could drop the car into a lower gear (assuming the vehicle has a manual gearbox), apply the handbrake (which is independent of the foot brake) or even put the car into reverse (with expensive results for the gearbox). There is less scope with an automatic gearbox but putting it into reverse could work if the electronics permitted. Switching off the engine would also slow down the car although this would also disable the power steering, if fitted, and make the car impossible to handle. Of course, the car could still skid and fall off the winding mountain road, as the would-be killer intended, but as a method of murder this is far from infallible.

Strangulation

Attempting to knock someone out by half-strangling them has been covered in Chapter 3 but in many scenarios the attacker intends to kill. Compressing someone's neck or throat, with a ligature or manually, can affect several vital structures depending on the force used and how it is applied. The jugular veins may be compressed which stops blood leaving the brain and will cause unconsciousness leading to death if the pressure is maintained. It takes around 4.4lbs of pressure to do this - equivalent to a couple of bags of sugar.

Further pressure - 5.5-22lbs - will compress the carotid arteries, preventing blood reaching the brain with similar results to the above. A larger pressure (33lbs) on the trachea (windpipe) will compress it and prevent air from reaching the lungs, again causing unconsciousness and death[25].

Compressing either the jugulars or the carotids will cause unconsciousness in 10-15 seconds and death within minutes[26]. Similarly, complete compression of the airway will cause death within three to five minutes[27] although if some air can reach the lungs the victim may stay alive longer. If the victim survives any type of strangulation after losing consciousness there is always the possibility of brain damage[28]. The longer the brain is deprived of oxygen, the more serious any such damage will be.

A further possibility is vagal inhibition, where pressure on the neck just above the point at which the carotid artery divides leads to an impulse travelling down the vagus nerve to the heart. In sensitive individuals this can stop the heart and be fatal within seconds, or a couple of minutes at most, and is undetectable at autopsy[29]. (N.B. a defibrillator will not restart a stopped heart. It is used to treat ventricular fibrillation, where the part of the heart which pumps blood out to the body is simply fluttering, without a proper rhythm, rather than contracting properly).

A forensic point worth noting is that determining the handedness of a manual strangler cannot be reliably determined by examining the victim's neck[30] since the way assailants place their hands is variable. Estimates of hand size may be more reliable.

Suffocation

Suffocation is the prevention of breathing by obstructing the mouth and nose. Pillows, plastic bags and duct tape are all potential weapons and have been used in fact and fiction. Keeping a fit adult still enough for the three to five minutes necessary could be difficult but very young, elderly and infirm people are much more vulnerable. Anyone with impaired lung function, e.g. a smoker or someone with asthma or COPD, may not last as long. Compressing the chest so that it cannot expand to enable the lungs to take in air has the same result. Many deaths where crowds are involved, such as in the Hillsborough football stadium disaster where 96 people died[31], result from suffocation where people at the bottom of the pile cannot breathe because of the weight of people above them.

Analogous to suffocation is asphyxiation with a non-toxic gas which excludes oxygen from the lungs. William Burton McCormick used carbon dioxide as a murder weapon in the short story *Matricide and Ice Cream* (2017) and methane (natural gas) can kill by excluding air if someone has their head in an oven with the gas on, although they would need to be unconscious first. Val McDermid used this in *Splinter the Silence* (2015). Robert Galbraith's killer in *Lethal White* (2018) used helium as an asphyxiant, coupled with a sedative which prevented the victim from struggling.

Exploiting allergies

Many people suffer from allergies, some of which have become much more common in recent decades. A sensitive person coming into contact with an allergen may experience symptoms ranging from irritation and a rash to death from anaphylactic shock. A character who knows about a potential victim's vulnerability could take advantage of this by adding, for instance, powdered peanuts or sesame seeds to their food, with fatal results. The death could be passed off as an accident or blamed on the food supplier, especially if a ready meal or takeaway was involved. Whether something more overt, such as an airgun dart tipped with peanut butter, would work is open to debate. Death by allergy has been used in films - in *The Net*[b] a character's medical records were hacked to remove a reference to penicillin allergy and he received a fatal dose as a result, while Theresa Russell's character in the film *Black Widow*[c] killed her penicillin-allergic husband by spiking his toothpaste with the drug.

Part 2: Escaping and fighting back

Many novels involve a protagonist in captivity who needs to find some way of escaping, with or without overpowering the captor, and/or defending his or her self. This entails looking around the immediate environment for items that could be used as tools or weapons. Fighting back, or using physical effort to break out, is likely to be difficult for someone who has been underfed and under-exercised for any length of time but desperation could lend strength.

Breaking out

In a classic scenario someone manages to pick the lock on a door using a paper clip or the underwire from a bra. With no previous experience of breaking and entering, he or she manages to jiggle a piece of metal inside the lock mechanism and the door opens easily. So how feasible is this, without training or practice? The short answer is "Not very". If the lock is modern, well-oiled, reasonably simple and the improvised lockpick is strong enough it could work. There are numerous videos on *YouTube* demonstrating how to pick locks with hairpins or paperclips but someone locked in a cellar is unlikely to have access to the web. Still, they would have plenty of time to practise.

Two implements are needed to pick modern locks such as the Yale or mortice types - one to exert a turning force and one to move the pins or levers into the correct position for the lock to open. If the lock is old or rusty the force needed could be too large for a small paperclip to work so if you are planning to write this scenario into a story, try it yourself with a variety of implements. A flimsy piece of wire is unlikely to have much effect on an old-style, heavy door lock but something useful could, perhaps, be fashioned from a wire coat hanger or a bed-spring - assuming the captor is careless enough to leave such an item in the room. Considerable ingenuity may be required!

Breaking through the bricks or stones of a wall to escape is an even less likely prospect. Prison escape films which show someone chiselling the mortar from between the bricks in the cell wall using a piece of cutlery may have some credibility, given the length of time available and assuming there is a sufficient supply of implements. Someone trapped in a normal room or cellar with a dreadful fate impending is unlikely to have the time or facilities to dig out a passage. A dislodged brick, however, could be a useful weapon.

Some internal walls in older houses may be constructed of lath and plaster while, in newer ones, studs and plasterboard are used. These are often weaker than a door and repeated blows could make a hole sufficiently large to crawl through. A solid implement would be desirable but determined kicking could produce the desired effect, especially on plasterboard. Breaking out this way would take a little time and be noisy so the captor would have to be away from the premises for a while.

Smashing a window is another possible way out but it can be tricky to do this without sustaining cuts. Some glass is reinforced with wire for fire resistance and this is very difficult to break through. Modern glass at child level, e.g. in French doors, has to be laminated or toughened to prevent toddlers crashing through it and this is also very hard to break, although in older properties weaker glass may remain. Double glazing is also difficult to break through.

Lighting a fire to burn down a door is not a good idea. Unless the room is very large the smoke or lack of oxygen caused by the fire is likely to prove fatal before the door collapses.

Fighting back

If there is no feasible way of escaping from captivity unnoticed, another option is to overpower the jailer when he or she enters the room. In most cases the captive will be weaker than the captor and, possibly, in a drugged state. A weapon of some sort is clearly needed but your character would need sufficient strength to wield anything hard and heavy enough to do damage. The impact of something smallish and hard can be multiplied if it is swung in a sock - even sand or soil can be used in this way. In these circumstances it may be more effective to attack more vulnerable parts of the body such as kneecaps or ankles, to prevent pursuit, rather than to attempt to knock the captor out with a blow to the head. An initial blow from something heavy, however, could disorientate the captor sufficiently to do more focused damage.

Sharp implements could be devised, although remember that stab wounds don't usually put someone down quickly. Toothbrushes sharpened by rubbing them on brick or stone are common weapons in prison while a wooden chair leg could be broken and scraped to provide a sharp point. If you are thinking of having your character stab someone with an improvised weapon, e.g. the wire from a spiral-bound drawing pad (unlikely to work) or a coat hanger, try it yourself on a joint of meat before you write it.

A common mistake made by characters attempting to escape from captivity is to disable the jailer temporarily without ensuring that he or she is unable to follow. As a result they are quickly recaptured. While this may be desirable to maintain tension, it can be irritating - someone desperate to escape, not to say full of hatred for the person imprisoning them, would surely do a thorough job of disabling their enemy. They should also attempt to remove any weapons that could be used against them - so many films and TV shows have shown characters knocking someone over but leaving their guns behind.

A final note about knives. If someone is brandishing a knife it may be thought sensible to try to take it from them. There are videos on *YouTube* on how to do this and even self-defence classes. If you have a baseball bat or similar weapon you may be tempted to knock the knife out of the attacker's hand. Unless you are fit and have had plenty of practice at this type of activity it is unlikely to end well. A hand holding a knife is a small target and can move fast so, if you can, attack the assailant's arms or legs and keep as far away as possible from the blade.

Home discomforts

Another common scenario is the home invasion. Assuming your novel is set in the U.K., rather in than the U.S. where the use of firearms to defend the home is legal, the householder has a limited range of weapons available. There is, of course, the cliché of the knife block in the kitchen but most householders are not skilled knife fighters.

If your character picks up a knife to defend his or herself against an intruder or attacker, make sure they don't hold it with the blade pointing downwards, attempting to strike the assailant with an overhead blow, as in many slasher films.
The chances are they will miss and impale their own abdomen or thigh. They should hold the knife low and use an upward blow or aim for the target's limbs. Given the risks of dropping the knife and stabbing oneself, to say nothing of the legal implications of accidentally killing an unarmed burglar, a knife is probably not the best choice of defence weapons.

There are many objects in the home which could be used as weapons, from irons and kettles to tins of beans. Their efficacy depends on the skill of the householder and whether they can avoid panicking - which many people in this situation would do. A young housebreaker on drugs is likely to be desperate, more aggressive and better at fighting than the average householder so the person attacked would need to focus their fury and not hold back - easy advice to give but hard advice to follow.
It may well be safer to hide and call the police, although characters in novels and screenplays are notoriously lax about holding on to, or charging, their phones.

If physical force is a problem for your character they may be able to get help from various chemical products around the home. Aerosol sprays such as fly killers, air fresheners and spray polishes all have a strongly irritant effect on the eyes and could be used from a metre or so away. Most will not do permanent damage if the eyes are rinsed promptly - but please don't suggest the use of oven cleaners, which are highly corrosive to flesh. Vinegar, lemon juice, washing up liquid, shampoo and spirits all irritate the eyes and could give a victim time to escape or do more damage to the assailant. Chilli sauces, especially the more powerful ones, would have a similar effect to the police-issue PAVA sprays.

Throwing a flammable liquid such as methylated spirit over an attacker and lighting it would be a desperate and dangerous measure. The liquid may splash back on you, could set the house on fire, and could do more damage to the intruder than is legally reasonable (see below). It is possible to use an aerosol spray as a type of flamethrower by lighting the emerging spray (older products using non-flammable CFC propellants wouldn't work) but this would be dangerous and have a limited range. The element of surprise might be helpful, though. Various DIY products may slow down an attacker by virtue of their irritant properties but in most cases it would probably be more effective to hit the attacker with the tin.

Don't panic

Most householders are not trained in self-defence or unarmed combat and are not likely to react to a home invasion in the same way as a trained police officer or special forces soldier. While some people may confront a burglar with outrage and courage, ignoring self-preservation, many people will panic. Thinking clearly in such a situation, and reacting effectively, may not be possible and a professional criminal is likely to gain the upper hand, as is someone on drugs which may deaden any pain inflicted by the victim. (This is not an argument for the universal possession of firearms).

The legal position

In some countries it may be perfectly legal to shoot to kill when someone attacks you or breaks into your home. In the U.K.

the law imposes constraints on what is permissible and this is summed up by the phrase "reasonable force".

If a crime is taking place in your home you can protect yourself in "the heat of the moment" which means you can use a weapon (not an illegally held firearm) and you can use force to stop an intruder from escaping. You cannot set traps or continue to beat up an intruder once you are no longer in danger[32].

Three contrasting examples illustrate the principle of reasonable force. A farmer who shot a burglar in the back and killed him while he was attempting to escape was convicted of murder, later changed to manslaughter on appeal[33].

A pensioner who fatally stabbed one of two burglars during a scuffle in his kitchen was not prosecuted[34]. Two brothers chased a burglar, who had previously tied up one of them at knifepoint, and one beat the burglar severely with a cricket bat. Both were convicted of grievous bodily harm[35].

The same principle applies if you are attacked outside the home. You are allowed to use reasonable force in self defence and this can be quite extreme if you are genuinely in fear of your life. You are not allowed to use violence to punish or for revenge.

Kneeing someone in the groin or jabbing them in the eyes if they attempt to strangle you is likely to be considered reasonable force. Repeatedly kicking them in the head once they are on the ground is not.

Writing attacks and escapes

- If your novel is set in reality, rather than in, say, *Midsomer*[d] where catapulted wine bottles and killer cheeses have been used to dispatch victims, it is worth paying attention to the points discussed above.
- There is always room for ingenuity and your character could be imbued with special skills, such as unarmed combat training or escape techniques, which normal

people could not deploy.

- Unlike murder methods, escape techniques and devising improvised weapons and tools are things you can some times experiment with at home.
- Try to pick a lock with a paper clip or other improvised implement - see *YouTube*.
- Take a look around the kitchen or garage to see what could be used as a weapon.
- Don't, however, attempt to obtain illegal weapons manuals – it could get you arrested[36].

CHAPTER 8: AFTER THE EVENT - BODY DISPOSAL AND CLEAN UP

Part 1 - Cadavers

Once your protagonist has killed someone, either deliberately or accidentally, there is the awkward question of what to do with the body. This is a fairly urgent problem as within a day or two the deceased will start to smell - you could experiment by warming a leg of lamb to body temperature and leaving it in a (pet-free) room for a couple of days. This section discusses some of the problems involved in disposing of a body with reference to real and fictional examples.

Handling

An adult human body is heavy and the average weight of people is increasing. Furthermore, a fresh corpse is awkward to handle as it has no rigidity. Before writing about someone moving a body you may like to try moving a co-operative friend or relative who's obligingly playing dead (please don't do this on stairs and make sure you don't damage your back). Once rigor mortis has set in, the body may be easier to handle but it won't be any lighter. Rigor mortis (stiffening of the muscles) starts between two to six hours after death, develops over 12 hours and lasts 1-2 days, all depending on the ambient temperature[1].

Various devices have been used in print and on screen to move a body without attracting suspicion. One ploy is to roll it up in a carpet in order to carry it out to a vehicle. This is fine provided that two people are available. A large enough carpet would be fairly heavy without the presence of a corpse and a single person couldn't possible shift both at once - unless, perhaps, they are Lee Child's hero *Jack Reacher*. A sufficiently large suitcase could be used by one person, although a lift would be needed to move it between floors and getting it into a vehicle would be difficult. A sack is another possibility and a strong adult could maybe carry a not-too-large body in one - although blood and other fluids could seep through hessian, a traditional sacking material. A tough plastic sack, such as the type used to deliver sand and gravel to building sites, would work but ordinary bin bags are too small and too weak. Stronger bags for rubble are available and they could be doubled up or stuck together as appropriate.

A putrefying corpse would be even more difficult to move without leaving traces than a fresh one. Apart from the dreadful smell, fluids would leak from the body and an impervious container would be required. The builders' bags mentioned above are not waterproof and a stout plastic liner would be needed - the plastic used to wrap carpets or mattresses may be suitable if your killer can find one large enough and unpunctured. A large wheelie bin is a possibility but getting the remains into it without creating a mess would be difficult.

Dismemberment

One solution to the problem of handling a large and heavy corpse is to dismember it. This is a particularly gruesome task and requires a certain amount of butchering skill. Hand tools such as knives and saws will remove limbs and the head but some strength is needed and it can be messy. Even messier would be any attempt to dissect the abdomen - dealing with around eight metres of slippery and, if punctured, extremely smelly, intestines is not to be recommended.

Dismembering a body in most premises without leaving traces would be extremely difficult, even if you cover the floor with thick polythene (detectives might wonder why you bought this). Just using knives and hand saws would spread blood and other fluids over a wide area while power tools would send a fine mist of DNA-bearing evidence all over the room - including onto the ceiling. An axe would also spread material over a wide area especially if wielded with vigour. A bath could be used for some of this task but doing it in an acrylic model would leave tell-tale scratches from any blades used. See below for clean-up techniques and how traces can be detected.

There is no doubt that a dismembered corpse is easier to transport and dispose of, whether in suitcases, bin bags or other vessels but there are still risks during disposal. There is a greater chance of traces being left in vehicles and premises than with an intact body unless multiple wrappings are used.

Flushing body parts down the toilet is not a good idea – see the case study below.

Case study: Murder in Muswell Hill[2]

Dennis Nilsen lured gay or homeless men back to his flat in Muswell Hill (London, U.K.) where he strangled them and, in some cases, kept their bodies for prolonged periods. He would then dismember his victims and dispose of the remains by various means, notably by flushing them down the toilet. This led to his downfall when a neighbour discovered that the drains were blocked with human body parts and the police were called. Nilsen was convicted of six murders in 1983, although he was known to have killed at least six other men, and died in prison in 2018.

Simply dumping bin bags full of body parts is also risky since they can be discovered easily, if not by humans then by dogs, foxes and other wildlife - see the case of Anthony Hardy who killed three women and dismembered two of them, leaving their body parts in bags on the streets of Camden[3].

Burial

Burying a corpse is an obvious way to get rid of one but it isn't always as simple as portrayed in crime stories. If you have a large enough garden, incurious neighbours and no immediate plans to move house then it may be a feasible solution.

Provided that you dig deep enough, the body - or what's left of it - can remain undetected for many years. In January 2018 a Manchester woman was charged with the murder of her father, who had been missing for 10-15 years, after human remains were discovered in her garden following her confession at the local police station[4].

A change of ownership of the property, or police suspicions, could lead to the body being discovered and the owner or tenant at the estimated time of burial would be an obvious suspect.

Woodlands are popular burial sites in fiction and in real life Epping Forest, in Essex, (U.K.), is said (unverifiably) to be the last resting place of a number of East End villains and their victims. The problem with woods as a burial site is the trees or, more specifically, their roots. The surface layer of leaf litter and soft soil is easy to excavate but very soon the spade will hit a network of tree roots. Digging to any depth would be arduous, if not impossible, and a shallow grave would soon be disturbed by foxes, badgers and dogs.

Assuming your character can find a reasonably root-free patch of land there are still problems. Digging a deep enough hole is extremely hard work, especially in heavy clay soils. You may like to try digging one 60cm wide, 150 cm long and a metre deep in your garden or on an allotment to see how hard it is - and how long it takes. In some areas the soil is simply not deep enough for a grave, or there may be so many chunks of rock in the ground that a mechanical digger rather than a shovel is needed. Note that peat tends to preserve bodies submerged in it for many years so a body dropped in a bog may be identifiable decades after disposal.

A further problem is what to do with the soil. Excavated soil takes up much more space than compacted, undisturbed soil and the volume of material left when the hole has been filled in will be considerably greater than the volume of the body underneath. This will need to be disposed of and even a casual observer would spot a mound of earth or an area where the surface soil seems fresh and a different colour from its surroundings. This will change in time as the soil is weathered but will be noticeable for a while.

Apart from spread and disturbed soil there will be other indications that a body may have been buried. As the body decomposes the soil above it will tend to slump, leaving a suspicious depression in the ground. Also, the vegetation on the excavated area may differ from that on the surrounding land as new plants colonise the bare earth - a plot device used in an episode of *New Tricks*[a]. Nettles are known to grow on fresh graves and poppies germinate readily on disturbed ground - a phenomenon which provided a clue in an episode of *Foyle's War*[b].

It was long thought that burying a body in lime, either quicklime (calcium oxide), or slaked/hydrated lime (calcium hydroxide), would speed up decomposition. Modern research has shown this not to be true. Experiments on pig carcasses, which are often used in place of human bodies in this type of research, showed that lime initially slowed down the rate of decomposition although in the longer term there was little difference. Limed and unlimed pig carcasses were completely skeletonised after 42 months[5].

If an area is suspected as being a clandestine disposal site a number of techniques can be used to investigate it including cadaver dogs (victim recovery dogs) which can detect corpses long after burial, ground penetrating radar, and measurements of the electrical or magnetic properties of the soil[6]. Ground penetrating radar was used to detect some of the bodies buried by the serial killers Frederick and Rosemary West at 25 Cromwell Street, Gloucester, U.K[7].

Although not conventional burial, dropping a body down an old well, mineshaft or swallow-hole would be a feasible way of getting rid of it although there is always the risk that cavers might come across it in some types of underground site. If you are using real locations it's worth checking whether or not there is a caving club active in the area.

Landfills

Wrapping a body in black plastic bags and putting it in a dustbin in the hope that it would be buried in a landfill would be risky. It could be days before the bin is emptied and the smell would alert passers-by. Furthermore, the crushing machinery in the collection vehicle would break open the bag and make it possible for the body to be seen when the vehicle is emptied at the tip. Landfills are secure sites and it is not possible to deposit a corpse there surreptitiously - unless, of course, you work on the premises.

In the house

Some murderers have concealed the bodies of their victims inside the house. Dennis Nilsen (see above) put parts of his victims under the floor boards while the Rillington Place murderer,

John Christie (see p86), hid bodies under the floorboards and in an alcove within a kitchen wall. It seems incredible that the smell of decomposition did not alert someone but under some conditions mummification, rather than wet decomposition, may occur[8]. If the body is placed where warm, dry air can circulate it slowly dries out and odour is much reduced. Some of Christie's victims were only discovered after he had moved out and a new tenant broke through the hollow plaster when attempting to fix a shelf to the wall.

Fire

There are problems with burning bodies. A crematorium ensures that all parts of the body are exposed, for over two hours, to a temperature in excess of 760°C. This boils off the water (about 70% of our body mass) and burns away all organic material leaving just bone fragments which do not burn. It would be impossible to achieve these conditions in a domestic fire or on a bonfire although a dismembered body would be easier to handle in this way. Residues would remain - notably bones and teeth - and could be identified as human by a pathologist or forensic archaeologist.

A further problem is the smell - burning flesh has a characteristic odour. Dennis Nilsen burned parts of his victims on a communal bonfire but added a car tyre which produced an even worse odour to disguise the smell[9]. Furthermore, as M.W. Craven describes in *The Puppet Show* (2018), the contents of the intestines smell dreadful when put on a fire. Of course, if the body is inside a burning house the odour would be masked by the smoke.

Hospital incinerators have been used to dispose of human body parts, legally in real life and illegally in fiction, but the body would have to be dismembered first with all the attendant problems. Gaining access to the furnace could also be difficult unless your killer works on the premises or can get past the security measures intended to prevent unauthorised access.

Sometimes a body may be burned, not to dispose of it completely, but to disguise its identity. Unless the skeletal remains are free of identifiable features, such as healed fractures and metal items used to repair broken bones, this is unlikely to be successful. The removal of teeth from a corpse, to prevent identification from dental records, has featured in several books and films. If the bones are not too badly burned some DNA may remain and can be processed, although the greater the heat damage, the less reliable the DNA result[10].

Acids and alkalis

Chemicals have been used in attempts to destroy bodies on numerous occasions, the most notorious case being that of John Haigh - see case study.

Case study: The acid bath murderer[11]

In 1949 John Haigh was convicted of the murders of six people who he either clubbed or shot before dissolving their bodies in concentrated sulfuric acid, initially in a workshop in London, U.K. and, in the case of his last victim, in a storeroom at nearby Crawley. He did this for financial reasons, forging papers so he could sell his victims' property. Police searching the Crawley premises found documentary evidence implicating Haigh in the murder of his last victim but no body. With no drain available, Haigh could not dispose of the dissolved remains and sludge into the sewerage system as before so he poured them over a rubble pile behind the property. Unfortunately for him, not all the body had dissolved. Professor Keith Simpson, the pathologist on the case, spotted a human gallstone on the ground outside the storeroom and further examination of material collected at the scene yielded bones, body fat and, tellingly, dentures which were identified as belonging to Haigh's last victim[12].

In 2016, Stefano Brizzi was jailed for the murder of London police officer P.C. Gordon Semple, parts of whose body he attempted to dissolve in acid[13]. Press reports did not identify which acid was used but a sensationalist website reported that he had both hydrochloric acid (which it misidentified as hydrofluoric) and caustic soda on the premises[14]. Brazzi was unsuccessful in dissolving much of the body. If he mixed the two chemicals together this is unsurprising, since they neutralise each other.

Acids are good at breaking down many tissues and bones but they are far from perfect[15]. In a series of experiments on pig bones using acids and alkalis, only full-strength sulfuric acid was capable of completely dissolving the sample[16]. They are less effective at destroying fat which is why a considerable amount of human-derived fat was found on Haigh's premises (see case study above). Acids can take a considerable time to work, however, and a large quantity would be needed to destroy a human body. In 2007 Larissa Schuster, a Californian biochemist, was convicted, along with an accomplice, of killing her husband. Using a stun gun and chloroform to subdue Mr Schuster, the pair tipped him into a drum and poured in hydrochloric acid while he was still alive. His body did not dissolve completely and was found by investigators in his wife's storage lock-up[17].

The sludge resulting from dissolving a body in acid is easier to dispose of than an intact corpse but is malodorous and hazardous to handle because of residual acid.

A further problem is finding a suitable acid-proof vessel in which to carry out the destruction. A mild steel oil drum, for instance, would dissolve quicker than the body when filled with acids and some plastics may also be attacked. If you saw the TV series *Breaking Bad*[c] you will remember what happens if you put hydrofluoric acid, plus corpse, in a bath rather than in the appropriate plastic vessel (if you didn't, it ate its way through the bath, the floor and the ceiling below).

Getting hold of acids, in sufficient quantities, presents another problem - it would take more than a couple of one-litre bottles from a local hardware shop to dissolve a corpse. Sulfuric acid purchasers require a licence in the U.K. and buying it in any quantity would certainly attract suspicion, especially if you insisted on paying cash to avoid a paper trail. Hydrochloric acid is more readily available but, again, purchasing large amounts could be seen as suspicious. Hydrofluoric acid is not widely available and is extremely dangerous to handle (it attacks almost anything) so having your killer use this would not be credible. As for *Breaking Bad*, no college laboratory would hold the quantities of hydrofluoric acid which Walter White managed to steal.

Acids are not the only chemicals that can destroy tissues. Strong alkalis can also do the trick and these are particularly effective at dissolving fats. Sodium hydroxide, also known as caustic soda or lye, is widely available for use as a drain cleaner and its sales are unrestricted. It is sold in pellet form and must be (carefully) dissolved in water before use.

In Mexico in 2009, Santiago Meza claimed to have dissolved the bodies of 300 rival gang members in caustic soda for a drug cartel. The authorities believed him[18].

As with acids, dissolving corpses in caustic soda takes time and also gives rise to unpleasant smells and fumes. Strong alkalis are not as effective as acids in dissolving bones although, given time, they will render bones fragile and crumbly so that they can be easily pulverised[19].

Both acids and alkalis can obscure cut marks on bones[20] which could frustrate pathologists attempting to match weapons to damage so even if a skeleton is not dissolved completely its forensic value can be seriously compromised. On the other hand, traces of usable DNA can sometimes be obtained from bones which have been treated with strong acid[21].

You can watch a video of Professor Raychelle Burks' experiments on dissolving bone in acids and alkalis on the Royal Society of Chemistry website at rsc.li/2sTTWjr.

Steve Cavanagh describes a credible way of disposing of a corpse using sodium hydroxide in *Th1rt3en* (2018).

Organised criminal gangs may have the resources to dissolve their victims in chemicals but for the average person it is likely to prove too difficult, not to say dangerous. Without proper protective clothing and safety precautions it is easy for the untrained person to harm themselves either with acid burns or

through inhaling fumes. Lung damage was a clue to the culprit in a fairly recent novel which featured the use of hydrochloric acid to damage, although not destroy, a corpse.
If you are writing for the screen, ensure that the vessel containing the acid has room for the corpse - in an episode of *Taggart*[d] the drum of acid in question was nearly full before the body was added. Overflowing acid would have dissolved the perpetrators' shoes and severely burned their feet.

The residue will still need to be disposed of, be it a smelly sludge or a collection of bones. The volume of material left will be considerably greater than the volume of the corpse and not easy to dump without someone noticing, although liquid and semi-liquid waste could be disposed of into a sewer. As a plot device, chemical disposal could be used to delay identification - and as a failed means of total disposal which could lead to the culprit being caught.

Watery graves
Disposal of a body in water is a popular practice in fiction and in real life. The Mafia was famous for dumping victims at sea or in rivers with their feet encased in "cement shoes" to stop them resurfacing.

Throwing an unweighted corpse into a river is unlikely to be successful as a permanent means of disposal since it will float, especially when gases produced by internal decomposition make the body bloat and increase its buoyancy. River currents are unpredictable and the body may drift to the shore and become entangled in plants so if you are planning this for a character and have a specific river in mind it is worth talking to people who know the river, e.g. a boating club, to explore its feasibility.

Lakes are a possibility and a weighted corpse may not resurface. Unfortunately, for your killer, people use lakes for fishing, diving and other recreations so there is always the chance that the remains will be discovered. Burial at sea is much more likely to be successful provided that the corpse is not disposed of in fishing grounds where a trawler's net might bring it to the surface.

Case study: Unexpected preservation[22]

Margaret Hogg was killed by her husband in Surrey (U.K.) during an argument in 1976 but her body was not found until nearly eight years later, hundreds of miles from her home. Divers looking for a missing student in the Lake District were searching Wastwater, England's deepest lake, when they found Margaret wrapped in carpet and tied to a concrete block. The water was cold and deep, with little dissolved oxygen present, conditions which led Margaret's body fat to be converted to adipocere. This waxy layer preserved the body from decomposition so it was easily identifiable by friends. Her husband, convicted of manslaughter, perjury and obstructing a coroner, was sentenced to four years in prison.

Exotic ideas from fiction

Screenwriters have come up with numerous ingenious means for disposing of a body including a car crusher (*Goldfinger*[e]), a wood chipper (*Fargo*[f]), feeding it to pigs (*Snatch*[g]) and (implied) incorporation into haggis (*Taggart*[h]).

In Christopher Fowler's book *Hall of Mirrors* (2018) the killer attempts to destroy a body in an anaerobic digestion sewage treatment tank - this would have worked, in time, although the bones would not have been destroyed.

In all these scenarios some material would have been discoverable, if someone had looked for it, and the victim would have been identifiable through DNA analysis. Several authors have had the idea of putting the body in an already occupied coffin intended for cremation or burial and this is fine as long as no-one opens it or realises that the coffin is considerably heavier than it should be.

Part 2: Traces left behind

Cleaning up blood

If blood has been shed, anywhere but in a specially prepared room, the chances are that traces of it will be found.

Most writers know that bloodstains at a crime scene can be visualised by spraying the area with hydrogen peroxide, or sodium perborate, mixed with a chemical called luminol. The mixture reacts with haemoglobin in the blood and, when the room is darkened and an ultraviolet light is switched on, the bloodstains glow bright blue. Under certain circumstances, blood up to 17 years old can be visualised with luminol[23].

Unfortunately, other materials, including bleach, coffee and brown sugar, can also promote this reaction, giving a false positive result. To allow for this a confirmatory test may be performed on a suspected blood spot. A DNA profile may be needed to identify the species and, if the blood is human, to match it to an individual.

The cause of many false positives is the use of sodium perborate or hydrogen peroxide, both of which will react with numerous substances as well as blood. Recently, Chinese scientists discovered that artemisinin, a drug used to treat malaria, is much more selective when used in place of hydrogen peroxide or sodium perborate and is less likely to give a false positive. Furthermore, the test using artemisinin is much more sensitive than the traditional method and can detect blood diluted to 100,000 times its original state. A refinement to this new procedure is the use of a smartphone to take a photograph with a long exposure time, thereby detecting the faint blue glow from diluted stains the perpetrator has attempted to wash away[24].

Luminol is not the only substance used to reveal bloodstains. Other chemicals, including fluorescein and a trademarked luminol derivative called *Bluestar*®, can also be employed. Their sensitivities vary and the choice of chemical depends on the circumstances[25].

Removing blood from absorbent surfaces such as carpets is particularly difficult - even if it looks clean to the naked eye, detectable traces are likely to remain. Harder surfaces can be cleaned more successfully but, even then, traces can remain which luminol can detect. Painting over blood stains may conceal them to the naked eye but infra-red light can detect blood under several layers of paint[26] while luminol can pick up traces of blood under paint layers even when attempts to clean the surface before painting have been made[27].

Bleach can be used but whether it works or not will depend on the type of bleach. A chlorine bleach, which most household products are, will fade the stain but luminol will still react. An oxygen bleach, such as hydrogen peroxide, will destroy the haemoglobin and there will be no reaction with luminol[28].

An overly clean area in otherwise dirty premises can attract suspicion. Detectives investigating the disappearance of a woman in Bristol in 2017 noticed that the bathroom in a scruffy flat was spotless - this was because the killer had dismembered her body in the bath with a circular saw (the receipt for which was still on the premises) and cleaned up afterwards. The perpetrators were arrested when the woman's remains were found nearby and convictions followed[29].

Cleaning up DNA

If dealing with spilt blood is difficult, cleaning up DNA traces is even more so. Details of how DNA can permeate a crime scene, and the sensitivity of detection methods, appear in Chapter 9 but suffice it to say that it would be extremely difficult to remove all traces of DNA-bearing material from a scene.

Flakes of skin, stray hairs and tiny spots of blood - or other bodily fluids - are difficult to see and clean up without specialist equipment. All a murderer can do is hope that the CSIs will miss the smaller traces - unless he or she makes a point of swamping the scene with completely irrelevant DNA, such as animal blood, in the hope that the forensic scientists will not be able to separate out the useful material.

Cleaning a crime scene with bleach to destroy DNA is a common ploy in fiction but there are some problems with this. Chlorine bleaches have a strong odour which can persist for some time, possibly attracting suspicion from investigating officers. As the name indicates, bleaches will take the colour out of fabrics and other materials - a pink patch in the middle of a burgundy coloured carpet would be just as suspicious as a brown patch on a cream carpet. Ensuring that the bleach came into contact with all traces of DNA would not be easy, especially where rough surfaces are involved. A chlorine bleach will degrade DNA, which soap and non-chlorinated disinfectants won't, but it does not do so 100%[30].

Although degradation of DNA may reach a point where useful profiles may be difficult to obtain, bleach does not prevent the identification of the species which provided the blood[31]. Bleach can also interfere with the standard tests for human blood which may be used after luminol has identified possible bloodstains[32].

Sodium hydroxide will degrade DNA but also attacks many materials and is potentially dangerous to use. Ammonia may not destroy DNA but it can inhibit the polymerase chain reaction, used to amplify DNA in samples (see Chapter 9), which makes it more difficult to analyse.

Whether someone who has just committed a murder would be clear-headed and thorough enough to remove all the incriminating DNA from a room is, perhaps, doubtful especially given the sensitivity of modern detection techniques.

Concluding points

Before devising a means of body disposal it is worth identifying the purpose of the disposal. If it is a question of buying a couple of days time, e.g. in order to flee the country, something simple like hiding the corpse in a cupboard, a derelict house or under some floorboards will do.

Leaving the corpse in some deserted area of the country could delay its discovery, too. If more permanent disposal is required then your character will have to make more effort and have more resources available.

Very few scenarios would mean that the body could never be discovered but some, as shown above, provide better chances than others.
If the goal is complete destruction so that the victim can never be identified the challenges are greater, requiring several stages

each of which could leave traces. To improve the chances of getting away with it, it helps if the killer is above suspicion. Once the police and CSIs start looking there is always the chance that they will find circumstantial or physical evidence pointing to guilt.

A full forensic examination of a building is expensive and time-consuming so would not be undertaken unless the police had fairly strong grounds for doing so, especially as budgets are limited. This means that your killer could get away with a less than perfect clean up, at least for a while. Evidence persists, however, so short of burning down the house there is always the possibility of its discovery – especially if the killer's behaviour after the event, and during any police questioning, raised suspicions.

Writing disposal and clean up:

- Bodies are heavy and awkward to move - is your character strong enough?
- Anything your character does with the body is likely to leave traces somewhere.
- Digging a grave is much harder than it's portrayed on screen - especially if the character doing the digging is injured or the site is in woodland. It also takes a long time.
- Dismembering a corpse takes some skill, a strong stomach, can result in unpleasant smells and spreads DNA all over the place.
- Using chemicals to dispose of a body requires training, equipment, and a means of getting rid of the residues, while purchasing materials can leave a paper or electronic trail.
- Removing traces of blood and/or DNA from a crime scene is extremely difficult, requiring patience, skill and meticu-

lous attention to detail. Even then, traces may be left. Bleach can be messy and arouse suspicion.

- Once suspicion is aroused a full forensic search may be undertaken but there are budgetary constraints

CHAPTER 9 DNA

DNA revolutionised the identification of criminals, beginning with the conviction of Colin Pitchfork in 1988 (see case study on p189). So what is DNA and what, exactly, can it do for the detective? What are the limitations of using DNA and how reliable is it? This chapter will explain the basics of DNA analysis and interpretation and will discuss some of the problems of relying too much on one type of evidence.

Part 1: The basics

What is DNA?

The make-up of our bodies is determined by chromosomes, half of which we inherit from each parent. There are 46 of these, in 23 pairs, in nearly all cells. Sperm cells have only 23 chromosomes (half of each pair) which combine with 23 counterparts in the egg during fertilisation to produce 23 pairs once again. Red blood cells have no chromosomes but white blood cells do, which is why blood is so useful for identification purposes.

Each chromosome is a tightly coiled molecule of DNA. The chromosomes are located in the nucleus of the cell but there is also DNA in structures called mitochondria which are present in the cell outside the nucleus. This can be important, as we shall see later.

DNA has been described as the genetic code. It contains within its structure instructions for the cell to make enzymes. Enzymes control what happens in the cell and how the building blocks of tissues, and hence all the structures in the body, are assembled.

Each pair of chromosomes controls a range of different functions but much of human DNA, with the current state of knowledge, appears to have no function at all (it is sometimes referred to as junk DNA). Those sections which produce an effect when the code is translated are known as genes. Other sections of DNA switch the genes on and off as required during the development of the organism. Some 99% of human DNA is the same, from person to person, but within the remaining 1% is the DNA which makes us individuals. The key point is that part of everybody's DNA is unique, apart from that of identical twins.

Generally, the DNA in any individual's tissues is the same, irrespective of where it occurs, (apart from that in sperm and egg cells) but there are circumstances where a mixture can be found. Transplanted organs will contain DNA from the donor and not the recipient, as will the white cells of transfused blood, although the latter will disappear from the circulation in time. Very occasionally an individual may have one set of chromosomes in some cells and a different set in the rest, a condition referred to as mosaicism. This normally results from a problem occurring shortly after fertilisation. Similar is the condition known as chimerism where two fertilised eggs fuse in the early stages of embryonic development. Again, two different sets of chromosomes are present. With appropriate research, these phenomena can be useful to a crime writer.

Collecting DNA

Almost any biological material found at a crime scene can be tested for DNA and such is the sensitivity of modern techniques that great care must be taken to avoid contamination. This is why crime scene investigators wear all-over protective clothing and face masks. The scenario where the detectives turn up at a crime scene before it has been thoroughly processed and just don a pair of gloves and overshoes is unrealistic - they would be shedding skin cells, dropping hairs and exhaling material all of which could contaminate the scene. Similarly, the scene where someone is wearing a forensic suit but peels back the hood and drops the face mask to talk to someone could result in contamination.

Obviously, first responders arriving at the scene of a murder or serious assault would need to check the victim and paramedics may need to provide treatment but the number of unprotected people entering the scene of a serious crime must be kept to a minimum. Similarly strict precautions to prevent contamination must be taken at the laboratories which analyse the samples - they are sterile, with filtered air, and their procedures ensure that all samples are kept separate (but see below). Blood is the best source of DNA with the chances of obtaining a useful profile from it being over 90%. From semen the success rate is 70% and from saliva it is 40%[1]. Hair with a follicle attached is also useful as are shed skin cells.

Analysis

Samples the size of a pinhead can provide useful DNA but, clearly, the more material there is to work with, the better and the more reliable is the result. Early techniques required a relatively large amount of material and there were problems with interference from other materials. These have been largely overcome and a key technique here is the use of the PCR (polymerase chain reaction). This is a means of amplifying the DNA present and involves using short segments of synthetic DNA, called primers, to bind to the sections of the DNA under test that are of interest. Varying the temperature of the mixture and adding a range of other chemicals enables these to be duplicated, doubling the amount of relevant DNA present. This is repeated 28 times or more, almost doubling the target DNA each cycle, although there are losses as the procedure is repeated. Commercial kits are used to carry out these processes in the laboratory and automated equipment enables many samples to be processed simultaneously.

The resulting mixture of amplified DNA fragments is separated into its individual components by a technique called electrophoresis. Early versions of the technique produced a series of bands on a sheet but these are now obsolete. Modern methods produce a series of peaks on a graph, each one corresponding to a specific fragment. This is the DNA profile.

It would be impractical and pointless to produce a complete map of all the genes in an individual's DNA (the genome). Instead, forensic techniques focus on areas of DNA which show considerable variation between individuals and are small enough to be analysed effectively. These sections of DNA are called short tandem repeats (STRs) and 16 of these sections (called loci) are amplified, as described above, and used to produce profiles. Some of the commercially available kits supplied to forensic laboratories can amplify up to 25 loci[2].

Although theoretically possible, the chances of two individuals sharing the same profile are extremely low (although the chances are higher in some populations where the opportunity to marry outside the group is restricted) and courts generally accept matches between crime scenes and suspects based on these profiles. The more loci are analysed the more reliable are the results and scientists can estimate the chances of two people sharing the same profile - the odds are usually several million to one against.

Sometimes only a partial profile can be obtained from material found at a crime scene - the sample may have decomposed or been altered by environmental conditions (degraded) or only a small amount of DNA may have been recoverable. A partial profile is still useful, however, both for aiding detection and eliminating the innocent but it must be interpreted with caution. As noted above, the smaller the number of loci used, the more likely it is that two individuals will share the same profile.

The false identification of Swindon resident Raymond Easton as a burglar operating in Bolton, on the basis of only six loci, led to him spending several months on remand until further DNA tests exonerated him[3]. Given that Mr Easton had Parkinson's disease and required substantial help to walk, this case underlines the inadvisability of relying solely on DNA as evidence of guilt.

In the U.K. DNA profiles of persons convicted of crimes are stored on a national database along with profiles obtained from samples collected at crime scenes. Anyone arrested has to provide a DNA sample (usually a cheek swab) but if they are found not guilty or released without charge the sample has to be destroyed by (U.K.) law.

Case study: The first conviction[4]

> The first criminal case involving DNA both exonerated the innocent and convicted the guilty. In 1983 in Narborough, Leicestershire, Lynda Mann was strangled and raped. Three years later the same happened to Dawn Ashworth. Richard Buckland was arrested and confessed (falsely) to killing Dawn but denied attacking Lynda. DNA from semen on the victims was compared with that of Richard Buckland and didn't match, thereby clearing him. Blood and saliva samples were then taken, voluntarily, from all adult men in the area but no match was found. An overheard conversation in a pub revealed that a local man, Colin Pitchfork, had paid a friend to impersonate him during the sampling. When Pitchfork was arrested his DNA matched and he was convicted of both murders.

Timings
In the early days of DNA profiling it could take weeks for the results to come back from the laboratory. Automation and improved analysis techniques brought the waiting time down to one to three days and there are now systems which aim to carry out the analysis in four hours or less[5]. One such system can process a sample in two hours - although it is not as reliable as conventional methods it can provide extremely useful information which would need to be backed up by other tests for use in court[6]. A semi-portable system, which could be used in a police station, would be ideal for checking the identity of a suspect against a database and enabling the police to keep a suspect in custody. It would not be suitable for processing crime scene material where the results are to be presented in court so confirmatory analyses using conventional methods must also be used. Since April 2017, there has been a 28-day limit on the time police can keep a suspect on bail so rapid processing of DNA samples has become particularly important.

Remember that forensic DNA work is done by commercial laboratories which may be overwhelmed with samples. The key factor in determining whether a result comes back quickly is where the sample is in the queue. In serious cases the work can be fast-tracked - at extra cost.

Mixtures of DNA

It is possible to separate the profiles of two or more subjects from a mixed sample although this is not always easy[7]. If the profiles of the individuals differ significantly the process is easier, but less so if the contributors are close blood relatives or only partial profiles are available. If one contributor's DNA overwhelms the other it can also be difficult to identify the presence of two individuals and if more than two people have contributed DNA the situation becomes even more complicated. Complex statistical processing, involving automated calculations, and skilled interpretation is often necessary to obtain useful information in these circumstances.

Case study: Interpretation errors[8]

In a major interlaboratory comparison exercise which took place in 2013, 108 U.S. labs were given the profile data (not the DNA samples) of a series of mixed samples and asked to interpret them using their usual protocols and statistical approaches. The exercise showed up variations in interpretation of mixed profiles between analysts in the same laboratories and also between different labs. With simple mixtures the results were reasonably consistent but with a four-person mixture which also included a spurious reference sample only seven laboratories correctly excluded the fifth sample.

Cold cases and sample storage

DNA has proved invaluable in solving cold cases. Viable DNA can be recovered from blood samples on evidence collected many years ago but this depends on how the sample has been stored in the meantime. Incorrect storage can lead to degradation of DNA over time but storing samples at very low temperatures, in the appropriate medium, can preserve the DNA for future testing[9].

Even when strict precautions have not been taken it is sometimes possible to obtain a DNA profile from a sample: in 2016 Christopher Hampton received a life sentence for murdering Melanie Road in 1984. A DNA profile recovered from the victim's clothing was traced to Hampton via a familial match (see below)[10].

Predicting appearance
Further information can be obtained from other parts of the DNA found at a crime scene, notably the sex of the person who left the sample (who is not necessarily the perpetrator) - a sex marker, called amelogenin, is routinely examined as the profile is constructed.

It is also possible to predict some aspects of a person's appearance and biogeographic ancestry from a DNA sample but this involves looking at specific genes rather than the STRs (see p187). This is known as forensic DNA phenotyping and only a few characteristics can be predicted with any accuracy at the moment.

By 2017, it was possible to predict whether someone's ancestry was African, Eurasian and East Asian with 97-100% accuracy; hair colour with 80-90% accuracy; and eye colour with 75-90% accuracy[11]. Evidence of sex is acceptable in court but DNA phenotyping is not although it can be a valuable tool for the detective.

Research continues and more characteristics may be predictable in future although many are determined by several different genes and are affected by environmental conditions during development and growth - height is an example - which make reliable predictions difficult. It is unlikely that a DNA sample from a crime scene will generate an e-fit style picture of a suspect any time soon.

Case studies: Right and wrong[12]

Spanish police used DNA phenotyping in the investigation of the rape and murder of student Eva Blanco Puig which took place in 1997. They were denied permission to take DNA samples from men in the area in which the crime occurred but later, in 2015, they carried out DNA phenotyping on semen found on the victim's body and determined that the attacker was of North African origin. Voluntary samples from North African volunteers who were living in the area in1997 generated partial matches with the DNA of two brothers. The police then arrested the third brother who gave a full match. He died in custody before he was brought to trial.

London's Metropolitan Police used an American firm to carry out DNA phenotyping on samples from a series of burglaries and rapes carried out between 1992 and 1999. The results suggested the perpetrator came from the Southern Caribbean so detectives flew out to Trinidad, with no success in finding the offender. When he was eventually caught he was found to have come from Jamaica, underlining the point that biogeographic profiling can only provide a broad indication of origins and not a precise identification of nationality.

Familial matches

Although everyone has a unique collection of genes (genotype) we all get roughly half our genes from our mothers and half from our fathers. We also share some genes with our siblings and with other relatives, although the number of genes in common decreases as relatives become more distant. The same rule applies for the STRs (see p187) used in crime investigation and this has enabled the police to identify potential suspects who have never been required to provide a DNA sample but have a relative convicted of an offence - which means their DNA would be on the national database. Partial matches with samples obtained from relatives can point the police in the direction of the real criminal.

Case study: M3 manslaughter[13]

The first prosecution resulting from familial DNA searching in the U.K. was that of Craig Harman in 2004. The previous year he had thrown a brick through the windscreen of a lorry travelling along the M3, resulting in the driver's death from heart failure. The partial DNA sample recovered from the brick, and complete DNA evidence from an attempted car theft nearby, produced no match on the national DNA database. Police then looked for partial matches and found 25 familial matches. A close relative of Craig Harman was identified and Harman himself was subsequently arrested and convicted of manslaughter.

Among other cases, familial DNA was used to identify the killer of Lynette White, murdered in Cardiff in 1988, some 15 years after her death[14].

In the U.S. a public access genealogy database called GED Match has been used to identify potential suspects in 21 murders. Run by a private company, the database was set up to enable people to trace relatives such as their biological parents - enquirers submit their DNA profile which is uploaded and the system identifies matches. As the database is not confidential, the police can provide DNA profiles from samples collected at crime scenes and a list of people related to the suspect is generated. Genealogical work then points to a likely perpetrator. There is no current equivalent in the U.K. but the Metropolitan Police, London, would be keen to use such a technique if it became available in Britain. There are ethical questions which must be addressed, however[15].

Mitochondrial DNA

The DNA used in the analyses described above is found in the nucleus of the cell and, as described, comes from both parents. There is another type - mitochondrial DNA - which is inherited only from the mother. Mitochondria are found outside the nucleus and are the powerhouses which drive the processes that go on in the cell. They contain simple loops of DNA which do not change much from individual to individual apart from two sections, known as hypervariable regions, where there is considerable variation between individuals. There is very little junk DNA and no STRs.

The advantage of mitochondrial DNA is that there are hundreds of copies of it in the cell (there is only one copy of nuclear DNA) so a sample which has been subject to degradation, e.g. through being heated, may still retain usable material. It is found in some samples which do not retain useful amounts of nuclear DNA, e.g. faeces (U.S.A.= feces) and hair shafts separated from the follicle. Old bones also retain mitochondrial DNA. Mitochondrial DNA is less useful for identifying suspects than is nuclear DNA but can be helpful in identifying degraded remains - the bodies of members of the Romanoff family, killed in the Russian Revolution, were identified using this technique and the U.S. military has used it to put names to the badly degraded bodies of U.S. servicemen killed overseas[16]. It can also be useful for eliminating suspects when samples do not match, enabling detectives to channel their investigations more effectively and clearing innocent people.

Low copy number

Low copy number (or low template number) analysis refers to the very high sensitivity of modern analysis and detection techniques. In favourable circumstances the DNA from a single cell can give a result and this brings with it problems, as will be seen later. Crime scene investigators without obvious body fluids to sample may take "touch" samples on doorknobs, glasses and other surfaces where there is no visible biological material. The few cells present may then provide information about who has been at the scene.

Part 2: Interpretation and complications

Identity

The first thing to remember is that a DNA match does not prove identity. Depending on the number of loci used and the quality of the sample a forensic scientist will be able to state that there is an extremely high probability that the sample came from the suspect but will not state categorically that this is the only person in the country with that profile. If the suspect comes from a restricted ethnic group, as mentioned above, the chances of someone else having the same profile are increased somewhat. It may be acceptable for a detective to talk about certainty in a briefing, or even while interviewing a suspect, but a scientist would not say so in court. This is particularly crucial when only a partial profile has been obtained. Although the Court of Appeal in the U.K. has ruled that a case can be brought before a jury solely on the basis of DNA evidence[17], DNA testimony should be backed up in court by other evidence to be sure of presenting a case that the defence cannot easily challenge.

Background DNA

DNA is everywhere. Professor Ruth Morgan, of University College London, has pointed out that you only have to be in a room for a minute to leave DNA traces[18]. The fact that someone's DNA is present at a crime scene does not mean that the person had anything to do with the crime - it could have been deposited there on a previous visit, long before the crime took place. Clearly some samples would be obviously linked to the crime but touch samples could be irrelevant. Even a bloodstain could be misleading if the innocent visitor sustained a cut or nosebleed while on the premises but, fortunately, the age of a bloodstain can be estimated with some reliability.

Secondary transfer

You leaf through a book in a bookshop/bookstore, sustaining a tiny paper cut as you do so and leaving a very small drop of blood on the cover. You decide not to buy and replace the book on the display. Ten minutes later someone else comes in, picks up the book and also replaces it. During this process, some of your blood is transferred to the book and then to the second person's hands. If they are then murdered shortly after leaving the shop, your DNA could be detected and you could become a suspect. This is an example of secondary transfer - DNA passing from one person to another even though they have never met. Similar scenarios could involve the seatbelts on a taxi, a bottle of wine at a party and even currency.

Persistence

Despite the fact that DNA can be degraded by elevated temperatures and a range of chemicals such as sodium hydroxide, bleach and hydrogen peroxide, it is remarkably persistent under some circumstances - the bones of King Richard III contained sufficient mitochondrial DNA to prove their identity. Research at University College, London, has shown that DNA from semen can be found on clothes washed several months after the deposit occurred. Also, clothes not previously contaminated can pick up semen DNA from being washed in the same machine[19].

How did it get there?

The phenomena described above underline the need to ask the question "How did the DNA get there?" Some cases are obvious - blood under the fingernails of the victim traceable to the scratched face of the suspect - but there could be perfectly innocent explanations for the presence of someone's DNA at a crime scene. In one British case, taxi driver David Butler was acquitted of the murder of a sex worker, Anne Marie Foy, whom he denied meeting, because his skin cells on her fingernail clippings and cardigan buttons could have come via secondary transfer from money which the accused, who had a medical condition which causes the shedding of large amounts of skin, had handled[20].

From the writer's point of view, background DNA and secondary transfer provide both an opportunity to demonstrate awareness of some of the problems involved in interpreting DNA and also a wonderful source of red herrings!

Contamination

The more sensitive sampling and analytical techniques become, the more they are at risk of contamination. As well as using forensic suits at the crime scene CSIs must ensure that all the equipment used to collect and package samples is free of biological material. Precautions should also be taken to ensure physical evidence, e.g. clothing and possible weapons, is not contaminated, either accidentally or deliberately during transport and storage. A defence lawyer will challenge evidence if it can be shown that accidental contamination had been possible.

The DNA profiles of U.K. police officers have been stored on the Police Elimination Database (PED) for some time but a more comprehensive database, the Contamination Elimination Database (CED), has been set up to include profiles from relevant people other than police officers. Some forces have been slow in transferring data from the PED to the CED and there has been opposition from the Police Staff Council to the compulsory inclusion of their members' profiles on the CED. An up-to-date and comprehensive CED is vital to prevent misidentification and wasted resources - the U.K. Forensic Science Regulator noted, in her 2017 report, that over 1,300 profiles thought to have been crime-related had, in fact, originated from police officers[21].

In the laboratory, stringent measures are in place to prevent contamination by extraneous DNA. Mistakes have been made, however, as in the case study below.

Case study: Laboratory error[22]

Cornishman Adam Scott was arrested on a charge of affray and his DNA was sampled. Shortly afterwards, he was arrested again, in Devon, and transported to Manchester to face a charge of rape, which he strongly denied. He spent five months on remand for rape until it was disclosed that his sample had contaminated the victim's in the laboratory as a result of poor procedures. A plastic tray, previously used for a sample from Mr Scott, was reused for material from the rape victim when it should have been destroyed. When this was discovered the rape charge was dropped although he remained in prison for another offence.

Writing DNA:

- DNA analysis is an incredibly powerful tool for the detection and conviction of criminals but it is important not to see it as infallible.

- DNA does not prove identity but a full match between profiles on a large number of loci make it extremely unlikely that another person is involved.

- DNA evidence in court should be backed up with other evidence to ensure a valid conviction.

- Ensure that, when you write a crime scene, all personnel tramping through it are properly dressed in forensic over suits, hair and shoe coverings and face masks.

- Partial matches may not be useful in court but can be helpful in identifying or eliminating a suspect.

- Interpretation is crucial - the presence of someone's DNA at a crime scene doesn't automatically mean they are the culprit. The key question is "How did it get there?"

- Humans and laboratories do make mistakes, both in handling samples and in interpreting results.

- Judges and juries do not necessarily understand the ramifications of DNA evidence and a lawyer's ability to present or challenge the evidence could be crucial.

CHAPTER 10: A FORENSIC MISCELLANY

Preamble
This chapter is not intended as a complete guide to forensic science. There are numerous books which cover the field, ranging from the popular to the postgraduate, and some are listed in references and further reading. Here I discuss a number of topics which could be of interest to crime writers and students, some of which may be familiar and some of which are novel. In some cases they represent an emerging technique which may not be deployed routinely. In others they may modify what we believe about existing techniques. I also include a discussion of the interpretation of forensic evidence and indicate some possible pitfalls.

There are two points to bear in mind with new techniques. Firstly, the fact that something can be done in a research laboratory does not mean that it can automatically be deployed in the field - practicality, costs and unavailability of skilled practitioners and equipment may act as barriers.

Many police forces would love to have access to the facilities shown in the *CSI:Somewhere*[a] labs on TV but simply don't. Budgets are tight hence the number of tests that can be requested is limited and crucial work may not be affordable. Secondly, it can take a long time before a new technique is recognised as providing acceptable evidence in court.

This does not mean it cannot be used in detection but it is important to recognise its limitations. Scientists are cautious beings, not prone to making statements they cannot back up, and this should be reflected in dialogue between police and practitioners. Nevertheless, an emerging technique can sometimes point detectives in the right direction and enable them to identify, or exclude, potential suspects.

A final issue to bear in mind is that the more sensitive a technique is, the greater the potential for contamination and false positives. Procedures to prevent this must be followed scrupulously.

Chemical analysis

Chemical analysis is not magic. You cannot simply put a drop of blood into a black box and find out, two minutes later, that a victim was poisoned nine hours and seventeen minutes previously by an obscure pesticide slipped into a shaken-not-stirred martini. The reality is much different and a diagnosis of poisoning will depend on the observation of any signs and recorded symptoms, the post-mortem detection of specific types of damage and analyses of samples. Some tests, noted below, give quick results while it can take months for the results of others to come back from the laboratory[1].

Certain materials, chocolate for instance, take a long time to prepare for analysis because of their complex mixture of ingredients. Note that there is no such thing as an undetectable poison, just poisons that someone might not look for or recognise the signs of at the post mortem.

There are some 2000 known poisons and illicit drugs[2] but very few of these would be tested for routinely. It is easier if you know what you are looking for - there is a battery of standard tests which may be performed on someone coming into hospital with suspected poisoning (the "tox screen" called for in TV programmes) but these will only look at the commoner substances, notably illegal or abused prescription drugs[3].

They use a sample of urine or blood and results can be back within minutes - necessarily if, for instance, treatments for overdoses are to be started.

Sometimes it can be difficult to obtain these samples, especially from someone who appears to be drunk. A saliva test for GHB has been developed which shows promise[4] while several other commonly misused drugs can also be detected in saliva, sometimes with portable devices[5]. Tests often involve sophisticated procedures and expensive equipment but for many purposes a simpler test for the identity of a substance is sufficient.

Spot testing drugs

If you are randomly searched at an airport and found to be carrying a bag of white powder you are likely to be politely

(depending on your appearance and attitude) detained while the contents of the bag are tested. You may insist that it is a perfectly legal dietary supplement, bought in Amsterdam where it is cheaper, but the suspicion will be that it is an illegal drug or possibly even an explosive. Simple, quick tests are now available to identify the major classes of controlled substances and they are used at airports. Naturally, if a test proves positive you will not be continuing your journey as planned but a clear negative result will enable you to regain your freedom.
These tests won't usually tell the officers what an innocuous substance is but will show what it is not. They will indicate whether a controlled drug is present but will not give any indication as to its purity - seized drugs are analysed more thoroughly to gather information on how much is there and from where it might have come[6].

Detectives in fiction have frequently tested suspected drugs by putting a sample on their tongues, the numbing sensation indicating that the white powder is cocaine. This is a seriously bad idea - what if the powder is fentanyl or one of its more lethal derivatives?

Sniffing it is also not recommended - there was a poster in a Bristol police station many years ago warning officers that dealers were cutting drug samples with the powder that makes up CS gas, in order to harm police officers seizing them, and on no account should they sniff confiscated samples. Presumably the product the dealers sold to users did not contain this eye-watering, choking material.

Spot tests for common drugs of abuse in urine are available readily and are sometimes used by employers and parents for drug screening. They can take the form of a dip stick or a chemical which changes colour in a specific way in the presence of the drug. Such tests do not give any indication of how much of the drug is present but merely show that it is there above a defined threshold concentration.

False positives
Sometimes a test can indicate that a person is a drug user when, in fact, they are not. Being in a room, or at a festival,

where cannabis is smoked could lead to a non-user giving a positive blood test for THC even though they did not actively smoke the drug. In 2014, the governor of Brixton prison tested positive for opiates after eating poppy seed bread. Inmates had complained that routine drug tests indicated they had been using opiates when they hadn't so the governor ate a slice of the bread and duly failed the test. Poppy seeds are no longer used in prison bakeries[7]. The case of the Birmingham Six, mentioned in Chapter 4, is another example of a false positive result. As previously noted, the more sensitive a technique is, the greater the possibility of a false positive result.

Residues and records

Detecting whether someone has been poisoned or drugged, especially if they are dead, isn't always straightforward. As noted in Chapter 1, the body gets rid of toxic materials by a number of means and some substances have a very short half-life. Often the breakdown products (metabolites) of the original substance are found rather than the substance itself - this is the case, for instance, with flunitrazepam and cocaine[8]. Furthermore, residues may be moved around the body after death so taking samples for analysis from the correct location is important[9].

How long drug residues can be detected in living (or very recently deceased) people varies according to the drug, the medium sampled and the dose taken. GHB is one of the quickest drugs of abuse to disappear - it is detectable in blood for only approximately five hours - while habitual users of cannabis may still excrete traces of the drug in their urine for up to three months[10].

Hair is the most useful medium for the long term detection of many residues. As it grows it picks up traces of chemicals from the bloodstream and this can provide a record of, for instance, substance abuse or episodes of poisoning. In 2016, the writer Helen Bailey was murdered by her partner and her body was hidden in a septic tank for three months. Despite the conditions in the tank, traces of the sleeping drug Zopiclone were found in her hair, indicating that she had been drugged repeatedly over a prolonged period[11]. Hair analysis also showed that Shannon Matthews, the nine-year old girl kidnapped by her mother and her lover's uncle (see Chapter 3), had been drugged with temazepam for some 20 months before she was kidnapped[12]. Analysis of elements in hair can also be used to track where a person lived while the hair was growing.

Fingernails, too, can provide similar information to that found in hair. Toxic chemicals such as arsenic are deposited in the nails as they grow, a phenomenon used by Dorothy L. Sayers in *Strong Poison* (1930). Analysis of oxygen isotopes in nails can show whether someone has recently moved into a particular area in the past three months[13].

Drugs and driving

It has long been illegal to drive under the influence of controlled drugs in the U.K. but, until recently, proving a driver's drug use has been difficult for the police. In 2015 two developments led to changes. Firstly, police can now administer a saliva test at the roadside which indicates whether the driver has taken cocaine or cannabis. Secondly, in England and Wales, legal driving limits have been set on blood levels of eight controlled drugs, eight prescription medicines and also amphetamine. The limits for illegal drugs are set low but someone accidentally exposed (e.g. by sitting next to someone smoking cannabis at a festival) is unlikely to exceed the limits. Anyone driving with more than the limit of an illegal drug or unprescribed listed medicine in their blood is committing an offence.

The limits for the prescribed medicines (benzodiazepines, morphine and methadone) are set higher than those for illegal drugs to allow for legitimate use. If the police believe that your driving is affected you can be arrested and compelled to take a blood test but if you are tested and exceed the limit for a prescribed medicine, the fact that you are taking it as instructed by a healthcare professional can provide a defence - as long as your driving is not impaired[14].

Portable spectrometers

A spectrometer is a device which measures, or detects, the presence of chemicals usually by determining what happens when the substance is exposed to radiation such as infra-red, ultra-violet or visible light. The mass spectrometer, an important instrument in many analytical laboratories, works differently by breaking up the molecules of substances under test into bits which are separated by sending them through a magnetic field. By identifying the fragments which result the scientist can reconstruct the original molecules and determine which substances were present originally. Spectrometers produce a characteristic pattern for each substance tested called a spectrum.

Most spectrometers are large, sensitive and expensive items of equipment but, increasingly, portable, handheld spectrometers are coming into use for such purposes as identifying the contents of suspect pills, measuring the sugar content of fruit, spotting counterfeit Scotch whisky and detecting explosives. They take readings and then compare the spectra they get with a library in the cloud, using Bluetooth and a mobile phone to make the connection. Some machines can identify the chemicals of interest through the walls of their containers, which promises quicker screening at airports and a safer means of investigating suspected explosive devices. Hand-held spectroscopy is still developing and is not yet a standard technique used by police forces. Specialists may have access to the technology, however, so it could feature in a plot[15].

Ionic errors

Some chemicals, including many poisons, are ionic in nature. This means that, when they dissolve in water, they split into two or more electrically charged fragments called ions. Potassium cyanide, for instance, splits into potassium ions and cyanide ions. When a blood sample is analysed the toxicologist will report that cyanide ions were found but not mention potassium ions - which are naturally present in higher concentrations in the blood - and certainly not potassium cyanide. Similarly, a report would refer to morphine, not morphine sulfate, strychnine, not strychnine hydrochloride and vecuronium, not vecuronium bromide. If the substances were analysed in tablets or a bottle, however, the full name would be reported. This is an easy error to avoid.

Down on the body farm

Studying what happens to a body between the time of death

and its discovery is the science of taphonomy. This is not an easy topic to study as facilities are scarce. A body farm (taphonomic research facility) has long been in operation in Tennessee, U.S.A, featuring in the novels of Patricia Cornwell, Simon Beckett and William Bass (who does this for a living) among others. Here, corpses are left to decompose under a range of conditions while scientists study the processes of decay. There are other body farms where human remains are studied in the U.S. but, so far, none in Europe although one is expected to be established in the Netherlands.

The climate in Tennessee is very different from that in the U.K. so data generated there may not be applicable in cooler conditions. Although there are no facilities studying human material in the U.K. there are five body farms which study animal remains sourced from abattoirs and pet shops (animals are not killed specifically for this research). In Wales (U.K.), for instance, Wrexham Glyndŵr University operates a body farm looking at a range of phenomena such as the effects of various blades on bone, decomposition of remains wrapped in a bag and what happens when material is encased in concrete[16]. While data from pig carcasses (which resemble humans in important respects) are undoubtedly useful human data would be even more valuable. There is a campaign for a shared human taphonomic research facility in the U.K. but there are legal and other issues which need to be overcome before one can be established.

Botanical barcodes

Pollen has long been a useful means of linking a person, or body, to a particular place. Expert palynologists can identify grains of pollen under a microscope and if the plant is restricted to a particular place, or type of environment, useful inferences can be drawn. Palynology is not used as much as it could be, according to a paper published in 2008, because it is labour-intensive, requires much expertise and experience, is inadequately funded and its crime-solving value is not fully appreciated[17].

Now, other parts of plants can be identified from their DNA. All 1,479 U.K. flowering plants have their DNA barcodes stored on a database which makes the identification of fragments of plant material relatively simple and quick. The project started with Welsh flora in 2005 and took nine years to complete[18].

Environmental DNA (traces found in water and soil) is used to determine the presence of various species in specific environments such as endangered newts in ponds[19]. Traces of environmental DNA could be used to link a suspect, or a victim, to a particular place provided that the DNA profile detected was on record. If your novel is set around a research establishment this may be a credible plot device.

Fingertip sex

Chemicals present in sweat, known as peptides, can enable forensic scientists to determine the sex of a person from their fingerprints. The relative abundance of these chemicals can determine whether the person leaving a fingermark is male or female, with an accuracy of 85%, and the process takes only ten minutes. It is also possible to determine the sex of someone, with a similar level of accuracy, by analysing the ridge density of their fingermarks but this requires clear and fairly complete marks rather than smaller, smudged examples[20].

Chemical lifestyle profiling

Using a technique called MALDI MSI it is possible to build up a picture of a suspect's lifestyle and dietary habits from chemicals found in fingermarks, providing valuable information for detectives. Traces of explosives, drugs, sunscreens, citrus fruits, wine and even the type of cooking oil used to prepare meals can be identified in fingermarks[21]. This technique has been pioneered by scientists at Sheffield Hallam University, U.K., who have demonstrated that it can be used in real life situations. In one instance a fingermark yielded traces of cocaine and also its metabolites, indicating that the depositor had consumed the drug and not simply handled it[22]. The technique is gaining acceptance and a simple hand-held kit is under development which will screen for cocaine, opiates, amphetamines and cannabis[23]. This could feasibly feature in a plot provided that your detectives have access to a friendly university undertaking this type of research.

Vein pattern analysis

Fingerprints have long been used to match suspects with scenes of crime but another biometric technique is becoming accepted by the courts. The patterns of veins, and other identifying features, on hands and arms are distinctive and individual. Where film of someone committing a crime exists, Professor Dame Sue Black and her team at Dundee University, Scotland, can often match these patterns to photographs of the suspect taken by the police. This is particularly useful in cases of sexual abuse by paedophiles (U.S.A. = pedophiles) who like to film themselves, with faces concealed, to enable them to relive the experience. In the first such case brought before a British court, in 2006, a teenager had used her computer to film her father allegedly abusing her. The judge accepted the evidence but, despite this, the jury did not believe that the father would abuse his daughter. In other cases, 82% of those charged changed their plea to guilty once they had seen the evidence and in 2009 Professor Black helped to break up a major paedophile ring in Scotland by identifying an oddly shaped white area (the lunula) at the base of the ringleader's fingernail[24].

Some 28 life sentences have been imposed on child abusers in the UK as a result of Professor Black's work on identifying hands and forearms. She is now leading a project to set up a searchable database of the anatomy and variation of the human hand, called H-unique, which will enable computers to match stored images with suspects[25].

In the U.S., the F.B.I. and the C.I.A. matched a vein in the hand of the man who beheaded journalist Daniel Pearl to images of the crime. They did this to support the killer's confession which had been obtained through waterboarding (torture) and might not have stood up in court[26].

Faking fingerprints

It is possible to fake fingerprints either by creating a false one to disguise your own, or by copying someone else's to mislead investigators (or to frame an innocent person). The former technique is relatively easy[27] while the latter requires some moderately sophisticated technology which is readily available[28]. A fake fingerprint featured in the R. Austin Freeman short story

The Red Thumb Mark (1907).

Fingerprints' pore relations

Conventional fingerprint analysis is based on examining the patterns of ridges on the skin. To do this effectively, and produce evidence that will stand up in court, a substantial part of the print is needed. A new technique, however, uses the patterns of pores in the skin to match even partial fingermarks and relies on the sweat which these pores secrete. The water in the sweat reacts with a chemical in a polymer film so that it appears red when irradiated with blue light. It is claimed that just 20-40 pores, in an area of $3mm^2$, are sufficient to produce a pattern capable of identifying the person who left the mark[29]. There is a long way to go before this technique can be used to convict a suspect in court but it could be useful for providing leads.

Dodgy documents

Detecting fraudulent documents, such as forged cheques and contracts, is a highly specialised discipline, requiring a detailed knowledge of inks, papers, printers and handwriting. It is not simply a question of looking at handwriting under a magnifying glass and offering an opinion - the work is carried out in fully-equipped laboratories with sophisticated equipment[30]. In the past it was relatively easy to trace a document back to the typewriter on which it was written but modern laser and inkjet printers are difficult to tell apart unless there is a defect which can affect the way the print appears[31].

A recent addition to the document examiner's armoury is the discovery, by scientists at Eurofins Forensic Services in Wolverhampton, U.K., of Ultra Violet Line Patterns (UVLPs). When examined under ultraviolet light, paper samples show a characteristic pattern of stripes running vertically down the sheet. These patterns vary in number, spacing and intensity from sample to sample and within the same ream they tend to repeat at regular intervals. This means that it may be possible to show that certain pages of a document have been substituted - e.g. to change a contract's details after the final page has been signed - or that invoices purporting to have come from different suppliers have been printed on the same paper[32].

Forensic gait analysis
The widespread use of CCTV and mobile phones provides a wealth of moving images showing people committing, or escaping from the scenes of, crimes. Attempts are often made to compare the gait of someone filmed in these circumstances with that of a suspect, as a means of identification. Such a comparison, known as forensic gait analysis, has provided evidence for use in court on occasions but such evidence must be viewed with caution.

There is no unequivocal scientific basis, methodology, or database of gait characteristics upon which the courts can depend. Also, there is no recognised professional qualification for forensic gait analysis although there are courses in forensic podiatry. Measurements of limb movements and angles are difficult to make with any accuracy, especially from blurry CCTV recordings, and gaits vary according to speed of walking, the activity involved, health and the influence of alcohol or drugs. No-one has a unique gait which can be replicated in all circumstances. For these reasons the Royal Society, in a primer for the courts, has raised doubts about the technique's validity[33].

If you are planning to use gait analysis in a plot it would be best for your detectives to use it cautiously for identification purposes, rather than as a means of providing key evidence for a conviction. After all, there is nothing to stop a criminal from putting something in a shoe to change the way they walk when committing a crime.

Gunshot audio
The prevalence of audio recording devices, such as mobile phones, dashboard cameras, some CCTV cameras and devices worn by police officers, is providing investigators with a new tool for investigating gunfire. Detailed analyses of gunshot recordings can identify individual types of weapon distinguishing for instance, between rifles, pistols and shotguns. Calibre, barrel length and whether a handgun is a revolver or a semi-automatic can also be determined. An array of microphones can provide data from which it is possible to determine where individuals involved in a shooting were standing and who fired first. Just such an array has been set up in 90 U.S. cities to

detect gunshots in real time[34].

Mistakes and reliability

Forensic science is frequently regarded as infallible. The numbers add up, the fingermarks match, the hairs are identical and the jury convicts - particularly if they are CSI[b] fans. In reality things can be very different. With the exception of DNA, which has a sound statistical basis and the expert can state the extremely low (millions to one against) probability of two people having the same profile, the interpretation of forensic evidence generally relies on humans. And humans can make mistakes, as can crime writers drawing on their work[35].

A match between fingermarks found at a crime scene and the fingerprints of a suspect was long taken as a gold standard of guilt. Provided that the two patterns had 16 points of similarity they were regarded as coming from the same person. There are two problems with this. Firstly, there is an assumption that no two people will have prints which match in the same way and therefore a fingerprint is unique to one person. There is no real evidence that this is in fact the case and there are not enough fingerprints recorded on databases to be able to say with certainty that two people cannot have similar fingerprints. The second problem is the human one. In one study of reliability five fingerprint examiners were given pairs of prints which they had stated were matches five years previously. They were told that the F.B.I. had misidentified the prints as matches and only one of the five examiners came to the same conclusion as he had previously[36].

Real cases of mismatched fingerprints include the prosecution of a police officer whose misidentified "print" was found at a crime scene she had never entered and the erroneous matching by the F.B.I. of a fingermark, on a bag of detonators linked to a train bombing in Madrid, with the prints of an innocent man who was kept in prison for two weeks as a result[37].

Partly as a result of the debacle over the misidentified police officer, fingerprint evidence is now regarded by the courts as opinion rather than an objective science[38].

Hair analysis has also come under scrutiny. A 2015 study by the F.B.I. looked at 268 cases where hair evidence had incriminated a suspect. In 257 cases (96%) erroneous statements were made and evidence was misinterpreted[39]. The technique in question involved examining hairs under a microscope and looking for matches. Nowadays, mitochondrial DNA in hair can provide a more reliable means of matching hair samples.

Hair analysis of a different kind proved problematical in Canada. The Motherisk drug testing lab analysed hair samples to determine whether they contained drug or alcohol residues which indicated substance abuse. They did this on behalf of child welfare agencies and between 2005 and 2015 tested over 24,000 hair samples. Following concerns raised in 2014, the Ontario government reviewed the laboratory and concluded that the drug and alcohol tests carried out during this period were inadequate and unreliable for use in protecting children or bringing criminal charges[40].

Other aspects of forensic science, such as identifying tool marks, shoeprints and even marks on bullets and cartridge cases, have also been challenged, particularly in the U.S.[41]. The arguments are that it cannot be proved that, for instance, the marks made by a particular tool on the remains of a pipe bomb are unique - i.e. that no other tool could have made the same marks. If there was a database showing the marks made by all similar tools on the same type of metal pipe then it would be possible to say that the marks were unique or to give a probability that only one tool in so many thousands would leave such marks. Such a database does not exist and evidence is thus based upon professional judgement, training and experience.

In the U.K., the courts still rely largely on the opinions of expert witnesses when it comes to forensic evidence. Provided that the witness is professionally competent, the subject under discussion is within his or her area of expertise, and the principles and methods involved are accepted within the forensic science community, the evidence will be given credence. Indeed, the performance of the witness under examination can be critical - a scientist who appears uncertain may be discredited by a skillful lawyer. Alternative opinions may be sought by the defence and a jury must then decide who is the most credible. In the U.S. the courts are beginning to require a more conventionally scientific approach. The criteria for an acceptable technique is that the underlying principles should have been empirically tested; that the theory behind it has been subject to peer review and published; that the error rate is known; that there are maintained standards for applying the technique; and that it is accepted by the relevant scientific community (these are known as the Daubert criteria).

Misinterpretation

Professor Ruth Morgan has said that "misinterpretation of forensic evidence is the biggest challenge facing forensic science"[42]. Even when the technical aspects of forensic evidence are valid, measurements are correct and the expert's opinion is sound, there are still opportunities for error. The best evidence can often be misinterpreted and to some extent this depends on how arguments are presented in court by lawyers who rarely have any scientific training. In 2017 the Jill Dando Institute (named after the murdered journalist in the case study below) carried out a study of successful appeals. In 22% of the cases examined evidence, including scientific evidence, was misinterpreted[43].

It is not enough to say that because trace evidence from a crime scene, whether it is DNA, a hair or gunshot residue, is present on a person they must have been at the scene. As noted in the previous chapter, the questions which must be answered are how and when it got there. It is entirely possible for trace evidence to appear on someone's clothing when they have been nowhere near the scene. Professor Morgan describes an experiment, carried out at the Jill Dando Institute, where someone fired a gun, picking up gunshot residue as a result. They then shook hands with someone else who, later, shook hands with a third person who tested positive for gunshot residue although neither the second or third person had fired a weapon[44]. Earlier, we mentioned secondary transfer in the context of DNA. This was tertiary transfer.

Trace evidence can be persistent on clothing, other objects and surfaces. In most cases it is impossible to tell when the material was deposited so someone could be placed at the scene of a crime which they had visited, for perfectly innocent reasons, long before the crime was committed.

There is a range of mechanisms and pathways by which contamination during the handling and processing of samples can happen, most of them completely innocent. If forensic evidence is the only evidence against a suspect then it is crucial that the prosecution demonstrates how the material was picked up by the suspect. In some cases this will be obvious - multiple hairs on someone's clothing consistent with an account of a fight, for instance. In others this may be more difficult - a couple of hairs could have come from two coats hanging on adjacent hangers in a nightclub.

Case study: A doubtful particle[45]

In April 1999 Jill Dando, a presenter of B.B.C.'s *Crimewatch*[c] programme, was shot dead outside her home. Thirteen months later Barry George was arrested for her murder and subsequently convicted. The evidence against him comprised witness statements, which later proved to be unreliable, and Barry Georges's behaviour - he had already been in trouble with the police. Crucially, a microscopic particle of gunshot residue was found in his overcoat pocket and at his trial expert witnesses suggested that it was likely that this came from a gun fired by George over a year previously.

Barry George appealed twice. On the first occasion his conviction was upheld but the second time the Court of Appeal was told that it was no more likely that the particle had come from a gun he fired than from another source such as contamination when his coat was collected and examined. The court ordered a retrial on this basis and the forensic evidence was excluded. Barry George was finally exonerated in 2008.

Misconduct
Genuine mistakes can be, and have been, made when collecting, processing and interpreting evidence but sometimes deliberate falsification can occur. Although deliberate planting of evidence seems to be rare it has happened.

In 2010 David Kofoed, the chief crime scene investigator for Douglas County, Nebraska, was sentenced to four years in prison for planting a speck of blood in a car, which led to the convictions of two innocent men for murder[46]. Between 1984 and 1992, six forensic officers employed by the New York Police Department fabricated fingerprint and other evidence to secure convictions. Their crimes prompted an overhaul of the rules governing the checking of fingerprint evidence[47].

Misconduct can also occur in the laboratory. Several major scandals have beset laboratories in the U.S. and the U.K., leading to arrests and prosecutions as well as many convicted people being released from jail. In 2014, forensic chemist Sonja Farak was convicted of tampering with evidence in drug cases and stealing drugs from the Massachusetts laboratory where she worked. As a result, the state district attorneys dismissed around 6,000 cases in which Farak was involved[48]. Even more damaging to the criminal justice system in Massachusetts was the conviction of Annie Dookhan the previous year. She worked in a state forensic lab and admitted to mixing up evidence samples and falsifying results. In consequence the state's highest court ruled that 21,500 cases in which she had been involved should be dismissed[49]. Similar, though smaller scale, cases have been reported in Texas, New Jersey, Montana and Canada[50].

In the U.K. the most serious case was that of Randox Testing Services, a Belfast, Northern Ireland, firm which carried out analyses for 42 police forces across the U.K. The company reported the improper manipulation of quality control data at their Manchester laboratory to the Forensic Science Regulator in January 2017, after discovering that batches of work that had failed quality control checks were misclassified as having passed them. Two people were arrested and some 10,000 cases, mainly relating to drink and drug driving, may have been

affected[51].
In May 2019, Britain's House of Lords Science and Technology Committee called for urgent reforms to forensic science provision and raised concerns about the use of unregulated forensic science providers that had not met the minimum quality standards required[52]. Shortly after, *The Guardian* reported that a digital forensics laboratory, used by a number of U.K. police forces, had been stripped of accreditation following alleged irregularities in handling evidence[53].

Writing forensics:

- Forensic science is a fascinating and fast developing field where new techniques are appearing all the time and old ones are subject to new scrutiny. These changes, and their interaction with human factors, provide scope for numerous plot devices.

- Remember that the scientific investigation of a crime is a team effort. The people who collect samples and evidence from a crime scene will not be the people who carry out the tests on them. They will certainly not conduct an au topsy or have any contact with witnesses.

- Prevention of contamination of a crime scene is crucial and anyone entering it is logged and must wear all-over protective clothing, including masks - not just gloves and booties.

- Samples collected may not be as clear and unambiguous as shown on TV programmes. They may be contaminated, incomplete or degraded.

- If you are planning to incorporate a newly-developed technique into a plot, try to talk to the person who developed it. Many academics are willing to discuss their work and point you in the right direction. If you don't understand at least the basics of what's going on, don't write about it.

- Note the limitations of some classical forensic techniques, as mentioned above - but see also some of the references and further reading.

- A detective may make a definite statement about evidence matching but an expert witness will be much more cir cumspect in court.

- Partial matches and evidence unsuitable for court can still be useful for generating a list of suspects but better evidence is needed for a conviction.

- Forensic evidence which eliminates a suspect can be just as useful as evidence which implicates a suspect.

- Human error, lost samples, lab unreliability and deliberate misconduct can all provide a rich source of plot twists.

- Misinterpretation of evidence by expert witness, and how evidence is presented by lawyers, can all lead to the wrong result in court. Juries familiar with CSI believe in forensic infallibility.

REFERENCES AND FURTHER INFORMATION
There are numerous books and web resources available on the topics covered in this book. Some are based on proper medical studies, court cases and case reports whereas others may be the result of hearsay. Quite often, mistakes may be repeated again and again - as is the case with chloroform described in Chapter 3. Some newspapers are notoriously sloppy with science and conspiracy websites have a logic all of their own. Wikipedia is often reliable and contains useful references which you can follow up if you need more detail although some may be highly technical. If in doubt, please check! U.S.A. readers should be aware that dates given below are given in the European form of date/month/year.

Chapter 1

1.	Gossel, T.A. and Bricker, J.D. (2001) *Principles of Clinical Toxicology.* 3rd edn. Boca Raton: CRC Press, p24.
2.	ibid.
3.	Midazolam injection - FDA prescribing information, side effects and uses. Drugs.com. Reviewed 01/11/18 [Online] https://www.drugs.com/pro/midazolam-injection.html
4.	Guo, W. et.al. (2015) 'Homicide by Sch from a syringe-like dart ejected by a compound crossbow', *Journal of Forensic and Legal Medicine,* 30 pp25-28
5.	Xing, J. et. al. (2016). 'Three homicides with darts tainted with succinylcholine': autopsy and toxicology, *International Journal of Legal Medicine.* 130 (6) pp1541-1545.
6.	Contreras, V. Sepulveda, P.O. and Shafer, S.L. (2011) 'Bioavailability of oral propofol in humans', International Society for Anaesthetic Pharmacology 2011 meeting abstracts [Online] https://isaponline.org/application/files/4214/7034/5605/ISAP_AM_2011_Abstracts_22.pdf
7.	Emsley, J. (2005) *Elements of Murder.* Oxford: O.U.P. Chapter 16.
8.	'Teacher died after sharing bottle and a half of wine with friend in garden, inquest told'. *The Independent* 08/06/19 [Online] https://www.independent.co.uk/news/teacher-death-cause-alcohol-consumption-bottle-wine-gill-howe-cleeve-primary-school-hull-a8946836.html
9.	Collins, B. (2018) 'Poison pass: the man who became immune to snake venom' *The Guardian* 11/02/18 [Online] https://www.theguardian.com/environment/2018/feb/11/poison-pass-the-man-who-became-immune-to-snake-venom-steve-ludwin

10.	Ohno, Y. (2009) 'The experimental approach to the murder case of aconite poisoning', *Journal of Toxicology: Toxin reviews*, 17 (1) pp1-11
11.	Emsley, J. (2008) *Molecules of Murder: Criminal Molecules and classic cases.* Cambridge: RSC Publishing pp57-9.
12.	Harkup, K. (2015). *A is for Arsenic: The Poisons of Agatha Christie.* London: Bloomsbury Sigma p116.
13.	Emsley, J. (2017) *More molecules of murder* p6. Cambridge: RSC Publishing
14.	Extance, A. (2018) 'Chemistry graduate student admits poisoning colleague with carcinogen' *Chemistry World* December 2018 p9
15.	'Anthrax' *Wikipedia* https://en.wikipedia.org/wiki/Anthrax.
16.	ibid.
17.	Jenner, R. and Undheim, E. (2017) *Venom.* London: Natural History Museum p79
18.	Pearlman, J. (2016) 'Young man is first to die from spider bite in Australia for 37 years' *The Telegraph* 12/04/16 [Online] https://www.telegraph.co.uk/news/2016/04/12/young-man-dies-after-spider-bite-during-australian-bush-walk/]
19.	Stolbach, A. (2018) 'No reported deaths from North American Black Widow spiders but three deaths from the antivenom, says Dr Levine from @USCMedTox' Tweet from Andrew Stolbach, MD, MPH @toxicologist12. 07/09/18.
20.	Stewart, Amy (2011) *Wicked Bugs* London: Timber Press
21.	Saner, E. (2018). 'Who let the snakes out - and what should you do if you find one in your bed?' *The Guardian* 06/08/18 [Online] https://theguardian.com/lifeandstyle/2018/aug/06/who-let-snakes-out-what-to-do-find-one-in-bed]
22.	Jenner, R. and Undheim *op. cit.*
23.	Caufield, C. (1989) *Multiple Exposures* London: Secker and Warburg.
24.	Moore, K. (2016) *The Radium Girls:* London: Simon and Schuster
25.	Emsley, J. (2008) *op. cit.* Chapter 10

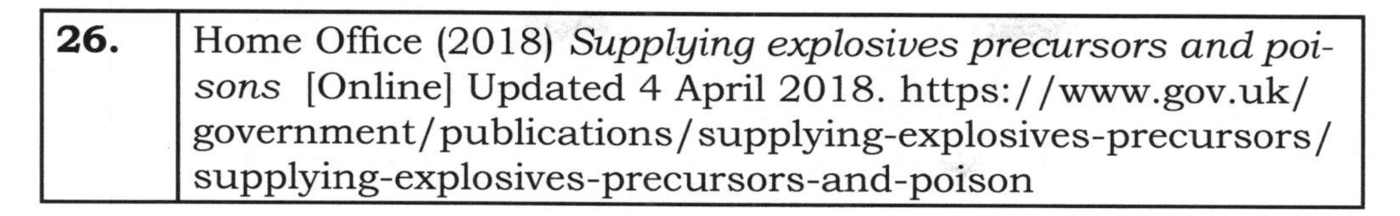

26.	Home Office (2018) *Supplying explosives precursors and poisons* [Online] Updated 4 April 2018. https://www.gov.uk/government/publications/supplying-explosives-precursors/supplying-explosives-precursors-and-poison

Chapter 2

1	Dickers, K.J. et al. (2003) 'Abrin poisoning', *Toxicological Reviews,* 22 (3) pp137-142.
2	Klein-Schwartz, W. (2017) 'Abrin' *ToxTid bits* July 2017 Maryland Poison Center. [Online] https://www.mdpoison.com/media/SOP/mdpoison-com/ToxTidbits/2017/July%202017%20ToxTidbits.pdf]
3	Mirror Online (2104) 'Woman cleared of Breaking Bad murder bid jailed for buying poison online' 07/11/14 https://www.mirror.co.uk/news/uk-news/breaking-bad-trial-woman-cleared-4588357]
4	Harkup, K. (2015). *A is for Arsenic: The Poisons of Agatha Christie.* London: Bloomsbury Sigma p146.
5	Chan, T.Y.K. (2009) 'Aconite poisoning'. *Clinical Toxicology,* 47 (4) pp279-285.
6	Harkup, K. *op. cit.* p146.
7	Gammell,C. (2010) 'Woman used rare poison in curry to kill lover' *Telegraph Online* 11/02/10 http://www.telegraph,co.uk/news/uknews/crime/7205804/Woman-used-rare-poison-in-curry-to-kill-ex-lover.html
8	Harkup, K. *op. cit.* p36
9	ibid. p38
10	*Wife guilty of Marine's arsenic murder* CNN.com International (2007) 01/02/07 [Online]http://edition.cnn.com/2007/LAW/01/30/arsenic.murder/index.html
11	*The Atlanta Journal-Constitution* (2018) 'Who are Georgia's most notorious serial killers?' 28/01/18 [Online] https://www.myajc.com/news/crime--law/who-are-georgia-most-notorious-serial-killers/3inDJTGdZ4NOWnu2mWjswM/
12	'Audrey Marie Hilley' *Wikipedia* https://en.wikipedia.org/wiki/Audrey_Marie_Hilley
13	Warder, R. (2014) '10 Horrific Poisoning Cases' *Listverse* 27/02/14 [Online] https://listverse.com/2014/02/27/10-horrific-poisoning-cases/

14	Whorton, J.C. (2010). *The Arsenic Century: How Victorian Britain was Poisoned at Home, Work and Play.* Oxford: O.U.P.
15	Emsley, J. (2008). *Molecules of Murder: Criminal Molecules and Classic Cases.* Cambridge: RSC Publishing p50
16	ibid.
17	*op. cit.* pp 61-6.
18	Weller, C. (2013) 'New botulinum toxin deemed deadliest substance ever: sniffing 13 billionths of a gram can kill', *Medical Daily* 15/10/13 [Online] https://www.medicaldaily.com/new-botulinum-toxin-deemed-deadliest-substance-ever-sniffing-13-billionths-gram-can-kill-259889
19	Gill, D.M. (1982) 'Bacterial toxins: a table of lethal amounts', *Microbiological Reviews*, 46 (1) pp86-94.
20	Feld, D. and Grünewald, R. (2018) 'Power of Poison', *The Biologist,* 65 (2) pp12-17
21	*CBS News* (2008) 'FDA warns of botox death risk' 08/02/08 [Online] https://www.cbsnews.com/news/fda-warns-of-botox-death-risk/
22	Emsley, J. (2008) *op. cit.* p142
23	*op. cit.* p143
24	Henderson, D., Young, D. and McHugh, M. (2010) 'Revealed: how evil dentist Colin Howell killed his wife and husband of former lover' *Coleraine Times* 01/12/10 [Online] https://www.colerainetimes.co.uk/news/revealed-how-evil-dentist-colin-howell-killed-his-wife-and-husband-of-former-lover-1-2359709
25	'Chemistry lecturer/physics lecturer/school teacher murders wife' [Online] https://www-student.cs.york.ac.uk/uni_history/murder.html
26	*Sky News,* (2018) 'Anaesthetist who killed wife and daughter with gas-filled yoga ball jailed for life' 20/09/18 [Online] https://news.sky.com/story/anaesthetist-who-killed-wife-and-daughter-with-gas-filled-yoga-ball-jailed-for-life-11502928
27	Mwangangi, J. (2011) 'Chlorine inhalation exposures' *ToxTidbits* June 2011 Maryland Poison Center [Online] https://mdpoison.com/media/SOP/mdpoison.com/ToxTidbits/2011/June%202011%20ToxTidbits.pdf

28	28. Nagesh, A. (2017) 'Mum almost died of chlorine poisoning from products she used to mop floor' *Metro* 07/08/17 [Online] https://metro.co.uk/2017/08/07/mum-almost-died-of-chlorine-poisoning-from-products-she-used-to-mop-floor-6835734/?ito=cbshare
29	Klein-Schwartz, W. (2017) 'Acute cyanide toxicity from amygdalin' *ToxTidbits* October 2017. Maryland Poison Center [Online] https://mdpoison.com/media/SOP/mdpoison.com/ToxTidbits/2017/October%202017%20ToxTidbits.pdf
30	*Death Unexplained* (2012) B.B.C. One Television, 07/02/12
31	Emsley, J. (2008) op. cit. p160
32	Harkup, K. op. cit. p85.
33	Emsley, J. (2008) op. cit. p161
34	Harkup, K. op. cit. p74
35	Agence France-Presse (2017) 'Japan's "Black Widow" sentenced to death for murdering a string of lovers' *The Guardian* 7/11/17 [Online] https://www.theguardian.com/world/2017/nov/07/japans-black-widow-sentenced-to-death-for-murdering-a-string-of-lovers
36	Beck, K. (2004) 'Poisoned painkiller panic: the Snow-Nickell cyanide murders' [Online] *History Link.org*. Posted 28/01/04 www.historylink.org/File5643]
37	Klein-Schwartz, W. *op.cit.*
38	Matthews, S. (2017) 'Cancer patient, 67, suffered cyanide poisoning from eating 2 teaspoons of apricot kernel extract each day' *Mail Online* 11/09/17. http://www.dailymail.co.uk/health/article-4872914/Cancer-patient-gets-cyanide-poisoning-apricot-kernels.html
39	Emsley, J. (2017) *More Molecules of Murder* Cambridge: Royal Society of Chemistry p135.
40	ibid.
41	Harkup, K. *op. cit.* p95.
42	Emsley, J. (2017). *op. cit.* p136.
43	*op. cit.* p141-2.
44	Stokes, P. (2005) 'Botanist killed himself by eating foxgloves' *Telegraph Online* 07/04/05. https://www.telegraph.co.uk/news/uknews/1487302/Botanist-killed-himself-by-eating-foxgloves.html

45	Office for National Statistics (2017) 'Number of deaths where dinitrophenol (DNP) was mentioned on the death certificate, England and Wales, 2007 to 2016' [Online] https://www.ons.gov.uk/peoplepopulationandcommunity/birthsdeathsandmarriages/deaths/adhocs/007648numberofdeathswheredinitrophenoldnpwasmentionedonthe deathcertificateenglandandwales2007to2016
46	Press Association (2018) 'Dealer of slimming pills found guilty of killing student, 21' *The Guardian* 28/06/18.
47	Mills, J. (2017) 'Young woman dies from diet pill overdose after hospital 'did nothing' '*Metro* 29/07/17 [Online] https://metro.co.uk/2017/07/29/young-woman-died-from-diet-pill-overdose-after-hospital-did-nothing-6815432/
48	Siddique, H. (2018) 'Care failure played part in woman's overdose death' *The Guardian* 15/02/18.
49	Gossel, T.A. and Bricker, J.D. (2001) *Principles of Clinical Toxicology* 3rd edn. Boca Raton: CRC Press p 255-6.
50	Press Association (2013) 'Christina Hale died after being poisoned by Death Cap mushroom, inquest hears' *Huffington Post* 07/09/13 [Online] https://www.huffingtonpost.co.uk/2013/05/09/christina-hale-woman-poisoned-death-cap mushroom_n_3245727.html]
51	Hargreaves, T. (2017) *Poisons and Poisonings: Death by Stealth.* Cambridge: Royal Society of Chemistry p80
52	*Wild Foodism* (2014) 'Tippler's bane and other mushrooms that don't go down so well with alcohol' [Online] https://wildfoodism.com/2014/11/06/tipplers-bane-and-other-mushrooms-that-don't-go-down-so-well-with-alcohol
53	Walker, P. (2015) 'Russian whistleblower had traces of rare poison in stomach, plant expert says' *The Guardian* 18/05/15 [Online] https://theguardian.com/uk-news/2015/may/18/russian-whistleblower-traces-poison-stomach-plant-expert-says-alexander-perepilichnyy-inquest/
54	Austin, J and Giannangeli, M. (2018) 'Alexander Perepilichny inquest delayed as Kremlin 'suspected over 14 UK deaths' *Express.* 07/07/18 [Online https://www,express.co.uk/news/world/968818/kremlin-Alexander-Perepilichny-russian-skripal-death-russian-whistleblower-putin.

55	Harding, L. et al. (2018) 'Russian fraud witness died of natural causes, coroner rules' *The Guardian* 20/12/18
56	Emsley, J. (2017) op. cit. p 92-93.
57	Dutt, V. et. al. (2010) 'The genus *Gelsemium*: an update', *Pharmacognosy Review*, 4 (8) pp185-194
58	Emsley, J. (2017) *op. cit.* p91
59	*op. cit.* p 97-98
60	*op. cit.* p187
61	Harkup, K. *op. cit.* p133
62	Emsley, J. (2017) *op. cit.* p189
63	Downs, C., et al. (2002) 'A hemlock water dropwort curry: a case of multiple poisoning' *Emergency Medicine Journal* 19 (5) [Online] http://dx.doi.org/10.1136/emj.19.5.472
64	Embury-Dennis, T. (2018) 'Deadly plant exposed on Cornwall beach in aftermath of storm Emma' *The Independent* 14/3/18. [Online] https://www.independent.co.uk/news/uk/home-news/deadly-plant-dead-mans-fingers-hemlock-water-dropworts-cornwall-beach-porthkidney-storm-emma-a8255416.html
65	Center for Disease Control (1994) 'Water hemlock poisoning - Maine 1992' *MMWR Weekly* 08/04/94 [Online] https://www.cdc.gov/mmwr/preview/mmwrhtml/00026056.htm
66	ibid.
67	Tampion, J. (1977) *Dangerous Plants.* Newton Abbott: David and Charles p93
68	Savill, R. (2006) 'Chemist used plant to commit suicide' *Telegraph Online* 06/10/06. https://www.telegraph.co.uk/news/1530689/Chemist-used-plant-to-commit-suicide.html
69	Marks, V. (2012) Quoted in *The Poison Review* 02/02/2012 [Online] http://www.thepoisonreview.com/2012/02/02/insulin-as-a-murder-weapon/
70	Marks, V. (1999) Murder by Insulin. *Medico-legal Journal* 67 (4) pp147-163
71	ibid.
72	Marks, V and Richmond, C (2007) *Insulin Murders.* London: Royal Society of Medicine Press
73	Parveen, N. (2018) 'Pharmacist convicted of killing wife in plan to start life with boyfriend' *The Guardian* 05/12/18.
74	'Beverley Gail Allitt' *Murderpedia* https://murderpedia.org/female.A/a/allitt-beverley.htm

75	Malamed, S.F. (ed.) 2018. 'Muscle relaxants (neuromuscular blocking drugs)' in *Sedation: A guide to patient management. 6th edition.* U.S.A.: Mosby
76	Xing, J. et. al. (2016). 'Three homicides with darts tainted with succinylcholine: autopsy and toxicology', *International Journal of Legal Medicine.* 130 (6) pp1541-1545
77	Malamed, S.F. *op. cit.*
78	'Dr Rubidium and JAYFK (2012). 'The history of sux, the world's most discrete murder weapon' *Gizmodo Australia* 29/05/12 [Online] https://www.gizmodo.com.au/2012/05/the-history-of-sux-the-worlds-most-discrete-murder-weap-on/
79	'Tokyo subway sarin attack' *Wikipedia* https://en.wikipediaorg/wiki/Tokyo_subway_sarin_attack
80	'Assassination of Kim Jong-nam' *Wikipedia* https://en.wikipedia.org/wiki/Assassination_of_Kim_Jong-nam
81	Chai, P. et. al. (2018) 'Novichok agents: a historical, current and toxicological perspective', *Toxicology Communications,* 2 (1) pp45-48.
82	Rawlinson, K. (2018) 'Survivor tells how nerve agent was hidden in perfume bottle' *The Guardian* 25/07/18.
83	Stoye, E. (2018) 'Novichok poisoning breakthrough as original container found', *Chemistry World,* August 2018 p8
84	Harkup,K. *op. cit.* p161
85	op. cit. p165
86	Morley, S. et al. (2017) 'Death from ingestion of E-liquid', *Journal of Emergency Medicine,* 53 pp862-4
87	Harkup, K. *op. cit.* p165
88	Gussow, L. (2018) 'Fatal ingestion of e-cigarette nicotine liquid' *The Poisons Review* 09/01/18 [Online] www.thepoisonreview.com/2018/01/09/fatal-ingestion-of-e-cigarette-nicotine-liquid/
89	Harkup, K. *op. cit.* p165
90	Gossel, T.A. and Bricker, J.D. *op. cit.* p169
91	Hydes, P. (2018) 'Lightning learning: nicotine poisoning' *East Midlands Emergency Medicine Educational Media* 23/7/2018 [Online] https://em3.org.uk/foamed/23/7/2018/lightning-learning-nicotine-poisoning
92	Morley, S. et. al. *op.cit.*

93	Robinson, W. (2014) 'Husband sentenced to life in prison for poisoning his wife 20 years ago with fatal nicotine dose so he could collect her $500,000 life insurance' Mail On-line 14/11/14. http://www.dailymail.co.uk/news/arti-cle-2835347/Man-sentenced-life-fatal-nicotine-poisoning.html
94	*The Guardian* (2018) 'Mother's fentanyl patch suspected as baby dies' 28/06/18
95	Emsley, J (2008) *op. cit.* Chapter 4
96	McKenna, A. and Erickson, K. (2016) 'The power of palytoxin' *Marine Aquarium Societies of North America* [Online] https://www.masna.org/masna-education/palytoxin/
97	*Evening Standard* (2018). 'Ten people in hospital after world's second deadliest poison Palytoxin leaks from fish tank in Oxfordshire village' 27/03/18 [Online] https://www.stand-ard.co.uk/news/uk/ten-people-in-hospital-after-worlds-second-deadliest-poison-leaks-from-fish-tank-in-oxford-shire-a3800526.html
98	Carrell, S. (2011) 'Gamekeeper with huge cache of bird poi-son fined £3,300' *The Guardian* 27/05/11 [Online] https://theguardian.com/uk/2011/may/27/gamekeeper-banned-pesticide-fined
99	Emsley, J. (2008*) op. cit.* p184
100	Shadnia, S. et.al. (2018) 'Delayed death following para-quat poisoning: three case reports and a literature review', *Toxicology Research*, 7 pp745-753
101	Emsley, J. (2008) *op. cit.* p184
102	*op. cit* p187-191
103	Harkup, K. (2016) 'Knickers in a twist: the case of the poi-soned pants' *The Guardian* 27/05/16 [Online] https://www.theguardian.com/science/blog/2016/may/27/knickers-in-a-twist-the-case-of-the-poisoned-pants-paraquat
104	Emsley, J. (2008) *op. cit.* pp191-196
105	CSB (2011) 'CSB investigation finds three DuPont accidents in Belle, West Virginia, resulted from numerous safety defi-ciencies including lack of safe equipment design, ineffective mechanical integrity programs and incomplete investigations of previous near misses' *CSB News Release* 07/07/11. U.S. Chemical Safety and Hazard Investigation Board [Online] https://www.csb.gov.

106	Gerritsen, W.B. and Buschmann, C.H. (1960) 'Phosgene poisoning caused by the use of chemical paint removers containing methylene chloride in ill-ventilated rooms heated by kerosene stoves', *British Journal of Industrial Medicine,* 17 pp187-189.
107	Emsley, J. (2017) *op. cit.* pp68-70
108	Warder, R. (2014). '10 horrific poisoning cases' *Listverse* 27/02/14 [Online] https://listverse.com/2014/02/27/10-horrific-poisoning-cases/
109	Harkup, K. (2015) *op. cit.* p226
110	Emsley, J. (2008) *op. cit.* p7
111	*op. cit.* Chapter 1
112	Metropolitan Police, quoted in B.B.C. (2018) 'The murder of Georgi Markov' *The Reunion* Broadcast on 31/08/18 [Online] https://www.bbc.co.uk/sounds/play/b0bgblcd
113	Starr, et. al. (2018) 'Suspected ricin detected in mail sent to Trump, Pentagon' *CNN online* 03/10/18 https://www.cnn.com/2018/10/02/politics/pentagon-ricin-mail/index.html
114	Emsley, J. (2008) *op. cit.* p106
115	ibid.
116	*op. cit.* p107
117	*op. cit.* p113-116
118	*op. cit.* p126-128
119	Tanner, P. et al. (1996) 'Tetrodotoxin poisoning associated with eating puffer fish transported from Japan - California 1996', *MMWR Weekly*, 17/05/96. 45 (19) pp389-391 [Online] https://wonder.cdc.gov/wonder/PrevGuid/m0041514/m0041514.asp
120	Gupta, P.K. (2016) 'Chemical food poisoning' *Fundamentals of toxicology: essential concepts and applications.* India: BS Publications
121	Cole, J.B. et al. (2015) 'Tetrodotoxin poisoning outbreak from imported dried puffer-fish Minneapolis, Minnesota, 2014. *MMWR Weekly*, 02/01/15 63 (51) pp1222-1225 [Online] https://www.cdc.gov./mmwr/preview/mmwrhtml/mm6351a2.htm
122	von Papineau, W. (n.d.) 'Newt toxins' *Caudata Culture* [Online] https://www.caudata.org/cc/articles/toxin2.shtml

123	*Mail Online* (2012) 'Man jailed for buying enough deadly puffer fish toxin to kill 20 people - but is cleared of plotting to use it to murder his wife' 25/09/12 http://www.dailymail.co.uk/news/article-2208176/Man-jailed-obtaining-deadly-puffer-fish-toxin-WASNT-trying-to-kill-wife-fantasized-special-military-agent
124	Harkup, K. (2015) *op. cit.* p261
125	Van Tassel, J.J. in Dominick, J.T. et al. (2004) *Crime scene investigation.* Pleasantville, NY: Reader's Digest pp122-3.
126	Repard, P. (2019) 'Ex-Navy man gets 3 life terms for poisoning wife at Dulzara home *The San Diego Union-Tribune* 14/03/19 {Online] http://https://www.sandiegouniontribune.com/news/courts/sd-me-uto-navy-poison-wife-sentenced-20190314-story.html

Further information for Chapters 1 and 2

The books by John Emsley and Kathryn Harkup referred to above are particularly useful.

Other titles which may be helpful are:

Cole, Leonard (2009) *The Anthrax Letters.* New York: Skyhorse Publishing

Jenner, R. and Undheim, E. *Venom.* London: Natural History Museum

Marks, V and Richmond, C (2007) *Insulin Murders.* London: Royal Society of Medicine Press

Stewart, Amy (2010) *Wicked Plants.* London: Timber Press

Stewart, Amy (2011) *Wicked Bugs.* London: Timber Press

Stratmann, L. (2016) *The Secret Poisoner: a Century of Murder.* New Haven and London: Yale University Press.

Whorton, J.C. (2010) *The Arsenic Century: How Victorian Britain was Poisoned at Home, Work and Play.* Oxford: OUP

Chapter 3

1	Payne, J.P. (1998) 'The criminal use of chloroform', *Anaesthesia,* 53 pp685-690
2	Stratmann, L (2005) *Chloroform: the quest for oblivion* Stroud: Sutton Publishing pp48-49
3	Payne, J.P. *op. cit.*
4	Stratmann, L. *op. cit.* p121

5	Kelly (2010) 'Classroom lab technician knocked out schoolgirl he tricked into wearing chloroform mask' *Mail Online* 25/08/10. https://www.dailymail.co.uk/news/article/-1305706/Star-pupil-chloroform-mask-ordeal-Lab-technician-knocked-schoolgirl.html
6	Vogt. C.R., Liao, J.C. and Sun, A.Y. (1980) 'Extraction and determination of chloroform in rat blood and tissues by gas chromatography-electron capture detection: distribution of chloroform in the animal body', *Clinical Chemistry* 26 (1) pp66-68
7	Stratmann, L. *op. cit.* pp166-185.
8	Fabian, R. (1955) *Fabian of the Yard.* U.K.: Heirloom Modern World Library pp214-219
9	Clegg, B. (2013) 'Chloral hydrate', *Chemistry World,* 27/03/13 Podcast https://www.chemistryworld.com/podcasts/chloral -hydrate/6112.article
10	Drugs.com (2018)'Midazolam injection - FDA prescribing information, side effects and uses' *Drugs.com* Reviewed 01/11/18 [Online] https://www.drugs.com/pro/midazolam-injection.html
11	ibid.
12	ibid.
13	CSRN Sedation Certification (n.d.) [Online] https://sedationcertification.com
14	Kelso, P. (2000) 'Male nurse used sedative to kill and rape' *The Guardian.* 18/05/00 [Online] https://theguardian.com/uk/2000/may/18/paulkelso
15	Drugs.com (2018) 'Ketamine injection' *Drugs.com* Reviewed 01/06/18 [Online] https://www.drugs.com./cdi/ketamine.html
16	ibid.
17	Drugs and Me (n.d.) 'Ketamine' [Online] https://www.drugsandme/en/drugs/ketamine/
18	NarcoCheck (n.d.) 'Ket Urine Test (Ketamine)' - manufacturer's leaflet [Online] https://www.narcocheck.com/en/urine-drug-tests/ketamine-test.html Tutorial notes.
19	Lupton. T and Pratt, O. (n.d.) 'Intravenous drugs used for the induction of anaesthesia' [Online] www.frca.co.uk/Documents/107%20-%20IV%20induction%20agents.pdf

20	Riviere, J.E and Papich, M.G. (ed). (2009) *Veterinary pharmacology and therapeutics* 9th edn. Wiley Blackwell p32. cited in Wikipedia.
21	*The Birmingham Post* (1998) 'I was framed from beyond the grave; vet tells how spurned wife made suicide look like murder' 29/07/1998 [Online] https://www.thefreelibrary.com/I+was+framed+from+beyond+the+grave%3b+Vet+tells+how+spurned+wife+made...-a060774455
22	Townsend, M. (2018) 'Dark web dealers stop sale of deadly fentanyl' *The Observer* 02/12/18.
23	ibid.
24	Verstraete, A.G. (2004) 'Detection times of drugs of abuse in blood, urine and oral fluid' *Therapeutic Drug Monitoring.* 26 (2) pp200-204.
25	Berry, A and Wainwright, M, (2008). 'Shannon given sleeping drugs for nearly two years, kidnap trial told' *The Guardian* 20/11/08 [Online] https://www.theguardian.com/uk/2008/nov/20/shannon-drugs-court-trial
26	Doward, J. (2019) 'Fake Valium sold online by drug gangs "is killing users" ' *The Observer* 3/2/19
27	'John Worboys' *Wikipedia* https://en.wikipedia.org/wiki/John_Worboys
28	Drug Enforcement Administration (2017) *Drugs of abuse: A DEA resource guide.* 2017 edn. Drug Enforcement Administration, U.S. Department of Justice. pp60-61
29	ibid.
30	Asthana, A. (2003) 'Men fall prey to date rape drug gangs' *The Observer* 21/12/03 [Online] https://www.theguardian.com/uk/2003/dec/21/ukcrime.gender
31	Atkins, N. (2012). 'A spoonful of death: How deadly 'coma in a bottle' drug GBL is legally available on the internet' *Mirror Online* 05/05/12. https://www.mirror.co.uk/uk-news/coma-in-a-bottle-drug-gbl-is-legally-819298
32	Jones, A. (2018) 'The G-spot' *The Guardian Weekend* 24/11/18.
33	Verstraete, A. *op. cit.*
34	'Stephen Port' *Wikipedia* https://en.wikipedia.org/wiki/Stephen_Port
35	Burks, R. (2018) 'Beating the scopolamine clock', *Chemistry World*, October 2018 p71.

36	'Hawley Harvey Crippen' *Wikipedia* https://en.wikipedia.org/wiki/Hawley_Harvey_Crippen
37	'John Christie (murderer)' https://en.*wikipedia*.org/wiki/John_Christie (murderer)
38	'Moscow theater hostage crisis' *Wikipedia* https:/en.wikipedia.org/wiki/Moscow_theater_hostage_crisis
39	*B.B.C. News Online* (2002) 'Russia names Moscow siege gas' news.bbc.co.uk/1/world/europe/2377563.stm
40	Davies, C. and Weaver, M. (2015) 'Burglars may have used gas during raid on F1 driver Button and his wife in St-Tropez villa' *The Guardian* 08/08/15
41	Lyle, D.P. (2016) 'Q and A: Can a blow to the head cause unconsciousness and amnesia?' *The Crime Fiction Writer's Blog* 05/04/16 [Online] https://writersforensicsblog.wordpress.com/2016/04/05/q-and-a-can-a-blow-to-the-head-cause-unconsciousness-and-amnesia/
42	Mayo Clinic (n.d.) 'Intracranial hematoma'. Patient Care and Health Information [Online] https://mayoclinic.org/diseases-conditions-/intracranial-hematoma/symptoms-causes/syc-20356145
43	ibid.
44	Doodles, M. (2018) 'Writing realistic injuries: Unconsciousness and head trauma' *Amino.* [Online] https://aminoapps.com/c/books/page/blog/writing-realistic-injuries-unconsciousness-and-head-trauma/7viP_u5qG-mKY3EZqkjRxe2N5Dr7ZYL
45	Thompson, T. (2015) 'Is it easy to knock someone out, without doing brain damage?' *Quora* 01/04/15 [Online] https://www.quora.com/Is-it-easy-to-knock-someone-out-without-doing-brain-damage/answer/Tommy-Thompson-10
46	Martial Arts Nerd (2018) 'Can a knife hand strike knockout or kill?' *Martial Arts Nerd* 26/01/18 [Online] https://martialartsnerd.com/can-knife-hand-strike-knockout-kill/

Further information

There is much material on the internet about the effects of date-rape and similar drugs but some of this should be interpreted with caution. Medical websites provide information about the use of anaesthetics in the clinical situation but this may not always be applicable in the criminal context. If you are thinking of using chloroform, Linda Stratmann's *Chloroform; the quest for oblivion* is essential reading as is the paper by Payne in the reference list.

Chapter 4

1	'Buncefield fire' *Wikipedia* https://en.wikipedia.org/wiki/Buncefield_fire
2	*The Herald* (2000) 'Lockerbie trial told of Semtex material traces' 03/06/00 [Online] https://www.heraldscotland.com/news/12235544.lockerbie-trial-told-of-semtex-material-traces/
3	'USS Cole bombing' *Wikipedia* https://en.wikipedia.org/wiki/USS_Cole_bombing
4	Ensign-Bickford Aerospace and Defense (n.d.) 'M122 Demolition Block' Manufacturer's product sheet [Online] https://www.eba-d.com/assets/product-sheets/M112-Demolition-Block-PrdctSht-for-Gen-Use.pdf
5	'Detonating cord' *Wikipedia* https://en.wikipedia.org/wiki/Detonating_cord
6	'Assassination of Airey Neave' *Wikipedia* https://en.wikipedia.org.wiki/Assassination_of_Airey_Neave
7	*The Guardian* (2018) 'Sharp rise in number of smuggled grenades' 20/08/18.
8	Sheve, T. (n.d.) 'How blast-resistant clothing works' [Online] https://science.howstuffworks.com.blast-resistant-clothing1.htm
9	Center for Disease Control (n.d.) 'Explosions and blast injuries: a primer for clinicians' [Online]https://www.cdc.gov/masstrauma/preparedness/primer.pdf
10	Hicks, R.R. et. al. (2010) 'Neurological effects of blast injury', *Journal of Trauma and Acute Care Surgery*, 68 (5) pp1257-1263
11	Health and Safety Executive (n.d.) *Explosion relief* [Online] www.hse.gov.uk/comah/sragtech/techmeasexplosio.htm
12	Ray, M. (n.d.) 'London bombings of 2005' *Encyclopaedia Britannica* [Online] https://www.britannica.com/event/London-bombings-of-2005
13	Buncombe, A. et.al. (1999) 'Two dead, 81 injured as nail bomb blasts gay pub in Soho' *The Independent Online* https://www.independent.co.uk/news/two-dead-81-injured-as-nail-bomb-blasts-gay-pub-in-soho-1096580.html
14	Fabian, R. (1955) *Fabian of the Yard.* U.K.:Heirloom Modern World Library p78

15	Bowcott, O. (2019) 'Inquest into 1974 IRA Guildford pub bombings to reopen' *The Guardian* 31/01/19 [Online] https://www.theguardian.com/uk-news/2019/jan31/inquest-into-1974-ira-guidford-pub-bombings-to-reopen
16	Robinson, P. (2015) 'Explosive chemistry', *Chemistry World* February 2015 pp46-49
17	'Acetone peroxide' *Wikipedia* https://en.wikipedia.org/wiki/Acetone_peroxide
18	Hamer, M. (1990) 'No forensic evidence against Birmingham Six' *New Scientist* 24/11/90 [Online] https://www.newscientist.com/article/mg12817441-800-no-forensic-evidence-against-birmingham-six/
19	'Semtex' *Wikipedia* https://en.wikipedia.org/wiki/Semtex
20	The Explosives Regulations 2014 [Online] www.legislation.gov.uk/uksi/2014/1638/made
21	Home Office (2018) 'Supplying explosives precursors and poisons' Updated 4 April 2018 [Online] https://www.gov.uk/government/publications/supplying-explosives-precursors/supplying-explosives-precursors-and-poison
22	Home Office (2019) 'Counter-Terrorism and Border Security Act 2019: Terrorism offences fact sheet' 11/02/19 [Online] https://assets.publishing.service.gov.uk/government/uploads/system/uploads/attachment_data/file/778108/2019-02-11_Terrorist_Offences_Fact_Sheet_RA.pdf
23	Gilfillan, A.J. (2017) Letter in *Chemistry World* January 2017 p4
24	Howells, S. (2018) 'Bishops Tawton bomb-maker jailed - and police tell how they caught him' *North Devon Gazette* 17/09/18 [Online] https://www.northdevongazette.co.uk./news/stephen-bracher-sentencing-bishops-tawton-1-5698841

Further information

There is much information about explosives and devices available via the internet, but see the caveats in the Chapter if you are proposing to investigate the more disreputable sources. Wikipedia has many pages about explosives and explosions although some of it is highly technical. It is a good source for incidents which have actually happened such as terrorist bombings, accidents like Buncefield and criminal prosecutions. The Government website .gov.uk should provide up-to-date information on the law and includes links to relevant legislation.

Chapter 5

1	Jackson, A.R.W., Jackson, J.M. and Mountain, H.M. (2008) *Forensic Science* 2nd edn. Harlow: Pearson Education p294.
2	Halliday, D. (2016) in White, P. *Crime scene to court: the essentials of forensic science* 4th edn. Cambridge: Royal Society of Chemistry p267
3	Garnish, S. (2016) 'Fact or fiction: Can your mobile phone blow up a petrol station?' *Scientific Scribbles* 08/10/16. The University of Melbourne [Online] https://blogs.unimelb.edu.au/sciencecommunication/2016/10/08/fact-or-fiction-can-your-mobile-phone-blow-up-a-petrol-station/
4	Jackson, A.R.W., Jackson, J.M. and Mountain, H.M. *op. cit.* p299
5	Trager, R. (2018) 'Criminal charges dismissed early against UCLA's Patrick Harran', *Chemistry World,* November 2018 p12
6	Jackson, A.R.W., Jackson, J.M. and Mountain, H.M. *op. cit.* p298
7	Halliday, D. (2016) *op. cit.* pp281-282
8	Jackson, A.R.W., Jackson, J.M. and Mountain, H.M. *op. cit.* pp 313-314
9	Halliday, D. (2016) *op. cit.* p268
10	ibid.
11	*op. cit.* p269
12	Jackson, A.R.W., Jackson, J.M. and Mountain, H.M. *op. cit.* p296
13	Halliday, D. (2016) *op. cit.* p270
14	*op. cit.* p279-80
15	*op. cit.* p281
16	Jackson, A.R.W, Jackson, J.M. and Mountain, H.M. *op. cit.* p316
17	*op. cit.* p318
18	Halliday, D. (2016) *op. cit.* pp 287-8
19	Bendelow, K. (2017) *The real CSI:A forensic handbook for crime writers.* Marlborough: Robert Hale pp123-4
20	Rogers, T. (2007) *Insultingly stupid movie physics.* Naperville, Illinois: Sourcebooks Hysteria pp273-7
21	*op. cit.* p281

22	*op.cit.* pp280-282
23	B.B.C. (2018) 'Ford to refund 'engine fail' EcoBoost customers' *BBC News Online* 01/10/18. https://www.bbc.co.uk/news/uk-england-45628325
24	Rogers, T. (2007) *op. cit.* p283

Further information

The references to this chapter contain much more detail than can be included in this book and you may also be able to get help from the fire prevention department of your local Fire and Rescue Service - although they will be unlikely to tell you how to start fires! In fiction, Don Winslow's *California Fire* and Life and Patricia Cornwell's *Point of Origin* both contain useful material while both Cara Hunter's *No Way Out* and Jane Casey's *After the fire* contain detailed and realistic accounts of fires and their consequences. For detailed accounts of numerous fires, deliberate and accidental, and their aftermaths see *Blaze: The forensics of fire* by Nicholas Faith - it is out of print but available second hand.

Chapter 6

1	Chandler, R. (1950) 'The simple art of murder,' *Saturday Review of Literature,* 15/04/50 pp13-14
2	Barrett Firearms (n.d) 'M107AI Owner's Manual' [Online] https://barrett.net/pdf/products/M107A1/M107A1-Manual.pdf
3	ibid.
4	'2017 Las Vegas shooting' *Wikipedia* https://en.wikipedia.org/wiki/2017_Las_Vegas_shooting
5	Lord Ashcroft (2015) 'Bodyguard who saved Princess Anne from kidnapper recalls moment he was shot during attack' *Mirror* 26/09/15 [Online] https://www.mirror.co.uk/news/uk-news/bodyguard-who-saved-princess-anne-6524307
6	Cross, R. (2013) '10 years after' *Airgun and Shooter* 01/09/13 [Online] http://www.airgunmagazine.co.uk/features/10-years-after/
7	Milroy, C.M. et.al. (1998) 'Air Weapon Fatalities', *Journal of Clinical Pathology,* 51 525-529
8	*B.B.C.* (2019) 'Stanley Metcalf: Great-grandfather admits airgun killing' 10/06/19 [Online] https://www.bbc.co.uk/news/uk-england-humber-48584698

9	Hastings, M. (1966) *The Other Mr Churchill.* London: Four Square Books pp201-205
10	BSAVA (n.d.) 'Dart guns' British Small Animal Veterinary Association [Online] https://www.bsava.com/Resources/Veterinary-resources/Medicines-Guide/Dart-guns
11	Hughes, M. (2010) 'Under starter's orders, the latest weapon to be outlawed' *The Independent* 17/04/10 [Online] https://www.independent.co.uk/news/uk/crime/under-starters-orders-the-latest-weapon-to-be-outlawed-1947204.html
12	Kostow, T. (2019) '3D printed gun report - all you need to know in 2019' *All3DP* 17/1/19 [Online] https://all3dp.com/3d-printed-gun-firearm-weapon-parts/
13	Tynan, D. (2018) 'Pistols printed by police blew up when fired' *The Guardian* 02/08/18
14	*The Guardian* 'Student facing trial for 3D-printing guns' 21/03/19
15	Harper. T. (2006) 'Deactivated guns made lethal in four minutes' *Telegraph* 24/12/06 [Online] https://www.telegraph.co.uk/news/uknews/1537748/Deactivated-guns-made-lethal-in-four-minutes.html
16	Newton, S. (2009) 'About effective range' [Online] http://gun-wiki.net/Gunwiki/FactorsOfEffectiveRange
17	Rice, B. (2016) in 'What is the average effective range of a 9mm round fired from a handgun?' *Quora* [Online] https://www.quora.com/What-is-the-average-effective-range-of-a-9mm-round-fired-from-a-handgun
18	*Telegraph* (2005) 'Gangs spread fear with 'spray and pray' weaponry' 18/03/05 [Online] https://www.telegraph.co.uk/news/1485936/Gangs-spread-fear-with-spray-and-pray-weaponry.html
19	Campbell, R.K. (2018) 'Handgun bullets: How do they penetrate in home materials?' *Gun Tests* Updated 13/11/18 [Online] https://www.gun-tests.com/issues/27_11/features/Handgun-Bullets-How-Do-They-Penetrate-in-Home-Materials-26552-1.html#.XBF8Atv7TIU
20	'Gunshot wound' *Wikipedia* https://en.wikipedia.org/wiki/Gunshot_wound
21	Daller, J.A. (2017) 'Can people survive gunshot wounds to the head?' *Medicine Net* [Online] https://www.medicinenet.com/surviving_a_gunshot_wound_to_the_head/views.htm
22	*TV Tropes* (n.d.) Short -Range shotgun [Online] https://tvtropes.org/pmwiki/pmwiki.php/Main/ShortRangeShotgun

23	Province of Manitoba (1959) 'Shotguns can kill at long range' Information Section, Department of Industry and Commerce, Province of Manitoba. (leaflet)
24	Crist, M. and Requarth, T. (2018) 'Forensic science put Jimmy Genrich in prison for 24 years. What if it wasn't science?' *The Nation* 26/02/18 [Online] https://www.the nation.com/article/the-crisis-of-american-forensics/
25	'Murder of Yvonne Fletcher' *Wikipedia* https://en.wikipedia.org/wiki/Murder_of_Yvonne_Fletcher
26	Barrett Firearms *op. cit.*
27	*Military Factory* (2016) 'Welrod (Assassin's pistol)' 02/11/16 [Online] https://www.militaryfactory.com/smallarms/detail.asp?smallarms_id=423
28	Arms Unlimited (n.d.) 'B&T VP9 *suppressed 9mm Welrod* pistol' [Catalogue online] https://www.armsunlimited.com/Brugger-Thomet-VP9-Suppressed-9mm-Welrod-Pistol-p/bt-410000.htm
29	'Linda Hamilton' *Wikipedia* https://en.wikipedia.org/wiki/Linda_Hamilton
30	'Dunblane massacre' *Wikipedia* https://en.wikipedia.org/wiki/Dunblane_massacre
31	31. Simpson, J. (2018) 'Border force agent smuggled guns and drugs' *The Times* 17/11/18.
32	*Ross Kemp and the armed police* (2018) ITV Television 6th September
33	*Express and Star* (2018) 'Three arrested as illegal gun factory uncovered at gearbox repair centre' 22/08/18 [Online] https://www.expressandstar.com/news/uk-news/2018/08/22/three-arrested-as-illegal-gun-factory-uncovered-at-gearbox-repair-centre/
34	Dodd, V. (2018) 'Police struggling to stop rise in illegal gun imports to U.K.' *The Guardian* 28/12/18
35	ibid.
36	Townsend, M. (2018) 'The journey of a gun' *The Observer* 18/11/18
37	Home Office (2016) *Guide on firearms licensing law 2016* [Online] https://www.gov.uk/government/publications/firearms-law-guidance-to-the-police-2012.
38	Sabbagh, D. (2018). 'Military-grade weapons ban dropped amid Tory objections' *The Guardian* 21/11/18

39	Reeder, M. (2019) 'How Harrogate man George Crossland was caught with 2.2 million indecent images of children and a cache of illegal weapons' *Harrogate Advertiser* 11/03/19 [Online] https://www.harrogateadvertiser.co.uk/news/how-harrogate-man-george-crossland-was-caught-with-2-2-million-indecent-images-of-children-and-a-cache-of-illegal-weapons-1-9643486/amp
40	Rogers, T. (2007) *Insultingly stupid movie physics*. Naperville, Illinois: Sourcebooks Hysteria
41	Evans, M. (2017) 'Counter terror police undergo specialist training on taking out lorry drivers who use vehicles as weapons' *Telegraph* 19/04/17 [Online] https://www.telegraph.co.uk/news/2017/04/19/counter-terror-police-undergo-specialist-training-taking-lorry/

Further Information

American gun enthusiasts post many videos online of themselves blowing holes in things and this can be a valuable source of material. There is plenty of information available about ranges, accuracy and magazine capacity of all kinds of weapon although there are sometimes lively disputes about individual performances. Wikipedia has much useful information about firearms in general and manufacturers' websites contain details of individual weapons' characteristics. Demonstrations of suppressors and the effects of different types of cartridge are also available online.

Chapter 7

1	Home Office (2018) 'Fire0601: Primary fires in dwellings and other buildings by cause of fire' [Online] https://www.gov.uk/government/statistical-data-sets/fire-statistics-data-tables#cause of fire
2	Home Office (2018) 'Fire 0602: Primary fires fatalities and non-fatal casualties by source of ignition' [Online] https://www.gov.uk/government/statistical-data-sets/fire-statistics-data-tables#cause of fire
3	JohnW2 (2019) 'Deaths due to electricity in UK'. Post on *DIYnot* online forum 28/1/19 [Online] https://www.diynot.com/diy/threads/deaths-due-to-electricity-in-uk.517228
4	Sehmer, J.M. (2009) 'Hair dryer in the bath not necessarily fatal' *Canadian Family Physician* 55 (9) p867.

5	Eleftheriou-Smith, L-M (2017) 'Apple iPhones should carry warning after man is electrocuted in bath, says coroner' *The Independent* 20/03/17 [Online] https://www.independent.co.uk/news/uk/home-news/apple-iphones-warning-electrocuted-bath-charging-richard-bull-ealing-west-london-coroner-sean-a7639961.html
6	Newman, T. (2017) 'Air embolism: Causes, symptoms and treatment' *Medical news today* [Online] https://www.medicalnewstoday.com/articles/186328.php
7	Fedschun, T. (2018) 'Texas nurse accused in patient deaths, leaving others in vegetative states charged with capital murder' *Fox news* 02/09/18 [Online] https://www.foxnews.com/us/texas-nurse-accused-in-patient-deaths-leaving-others-in-vegetative-states-charged-with-capital-murder
8	*B.B.C.* (2018) 'Catholic deacon accused of murder by air injection in Belgium' 22/01/18 [Online] https://www.bbc.co.uk/news/world-europe-42780226
9	Berghuis, K (2018) 'Nurse dubbed The Deacon of Death jailed over 'mercy killings' of five patients - including his own mum' *Mirror* 2/2/18 [Online] https://mirror.co.uk/news/world-news/nurse-dubbed-deacon-death-jailed-11958315
10	Marks, V and Richmond, C (2007) *Insulin murders.* London: Royal Society of Medicine Press p101.
11	'How powerful is a crossbow?' YouTube https://www.youtube.com/watch?v=hBia7_RNARc
12	*B.B.C.* (2018) 'Man wanted over crossbow murder found dead' 14/01/18 [Online] https://www.bbc.co.uk/news/uk-england-humber-42684785
13	*The Independent* (2018) 'Man gets life sentence for killing father with crossbow and hiding body in freezer' 08/06/18 [Online] https://www.independent.co.uk/news/world/americas/maxwell-carl-goldberg-murder-crossbow-hannibal-life-sentence-las-vegas-a8389751.html
14	*Toronto Sun* (2017) 'Crossbow killer Brett Ryan murdered family to hide his deceit' 28/07/18 [Online] https://torontosun.com/2017/07/28/crossbow-killer-brett-ryan-murdered-family-members-to-hide-his-deceit/wcm/97b926ff-ac1d-4cc9-9116-912861016aee

15	Press Association (2019) 'Man, 74, shot with crossbow bolt in north Wales dies ' *The Guardian* 11/05/19 [Online] https://www.theguardian.com/uk-news/2019/may/11/gerald-corrigan-man-74-shot-with-crossbow-bolt-in-north-wales-dies
16	Shepherd, R. (2018) *Unnatural causes.* England: Michael Joseph p193
17	Office for National Statistics (2018) 'Homicide in England and Wales: year ending March 2017' [Online] https://www.ons.gov.uk/peoplepopulationandcommunity/crimeandjustice/articles/homicideinenglandandwales/yearendingmarch2017.
18	Campbell, D. (2018) 'Doctors *treat huge rise in cases of life-threatening stab injuries' The Guardian* 22/10/18.
19	ibid.
20	ibid
21	Taylor, R. (2017) 'Horrifying moment boy, 16, kills man with one punch as he shows off to his friends' *Mirror online* 04/10/17 https://mirror.co.uk/news/uk-news/horrifying-moment-boy-kills-11284008
22	*B.B.C.* (2018) 'James McDonagh: Man is jailed for one-punch death' 16/02/18 [Online] https://www.bbc.co.uk/news-northern-ireland-foyle-west-43086614
23	Lyle, D.P. (2012) 'Q&A: Can a blow to the chest kill an adult male?' The crime fiction writer's blog 02/05/12 [Online] https://writersforensicsblog.wordpress.com/2012/05/02q-and-a-can-a-blow-to-the-chest-kill-an-adult-male/
24	Batalis, N.I. (2016) 'Forensic autopsy of blunt force trauma' Medscape 02/03/16 [Online] https://emedicine.medscape.com/article/1680107-overview.
25	Graham, M.A. (2016) 'Pathology of asphyxial death' Med-scape 24/01/16 [Online] https://emedicine.medscape.com./article/1988699-overview
26	Harle, M. (2017) 'Pathology Outlines - Asphyxia' Pathology Outlines.com Inc. [Online] http://www.pathologyoutlines.com/topic/forensicsasphyxia.html
27	Dolinak, D., Matshes, E.W. and Lew, E.O. (2005). *Forensic pathology.* Burlington, Maryland: Elsevier Academic Press p209

28	Sorensen, S.B., Joshi, M. and Sivitz, E. (2014) 'A systematic review of the epidemiology of non-fatal strangulation, a human rights and health concern', *American Journal of Public Health*, 104 (11) pp54-61.
29	Health Drip (2012) 'Vagal inhibition' 31/05/12 [Online] http://healthdrip.com/vagal-inhibition/
30	Graham, M.A. (2016) op. cit.
31	'Hillsborough disaster' *Wikipedia* https://en.wikipedia.org/wiki/Hillsborough_disaster
32	Crown Prosecution Service (2013) 'Householders and the use of force against intruders: Joint public statement from the Crown Prosecution Service and the Association of Chief Police Officers' [Online] https://www.cps.gov.uk/sites/default/files/documents/publications/householders-2013.pdf
33	'Tony Martin (farmer)' *Wikipedia* https://en.wikipedia.org/wiki/Tony_Martin_(farmer)
34	*B.B.C.* (2018) 'Hither Green 'burglary death' suspect to face no action' 06/04/18 [Online] https://www.bbc.co.uk/news/uk-england-london-43676359
35	*Evening Standard* (2010) 'Set free: Man who beat armed intruder with cricket bat' 20/01/10 [Online] https://www.standard.co.uk/news/set-free-man-who-beat-armed-intruder-with-cricket-bat-6776369.html
36	Press Association (2018) 'Alleged neo-Nazi terrorist posed in KKK robes while holding his baby, jury told' *The Guardian* 16/10/18.

Chapter 8

1	Bendelow, K. (2017). *The real CSI: a forensic handbook for crime writers.* Marlborough: Robert Hale pp23-24
2	*The Independent* (2018) 'Dennis Nilsen death: Serial killer who murdered at least 12 young men dies in prison aged 72' 12/07/18 [Online] https://independent.co.uk/news/uk/home-news/dennis-nilsen-death-serial-killer-young-men-victims-muswell-hill-murderer-prison-cause-a8349001.html
3	*The Guardian* 'Life for killer who mutilated women' 26/11/03 [Online] https://www.the guardian.com/uk/2003/nov/26/ukcrime/rebeccaallison

4	*Telegraph* (2018) 'Body found buried in garden: Woman charged with murder after remains of 'her father' discovered' 11/01/18 [Online] https://www.telegraph.co.uk/news/2018/01/11/body-found-buried-garden-woman-charged-murder-remains-father/
5	Schotsman, E.M.J et al. (2014). 'Long-term effects of hydrated lime and quicklime on the decay of human remains using pig cadavers as human body analogues: field experiments', *Forensic Science International,* 238 pp141.e1-141e13.
6	'Fred West' *Wikipedia* https://en.wikipedia.org/wiki/Fred_West
7	Harrison, K and Simmons, T. in White, P.C. (ed.) (2016) *Crime scene to court: The essentials of forensic science* 4th edn. Cambridge: Royal Society of Chemistry p571.
8	Jackson, A.R.W., Jackson, J.M. and Mountain, H.M. (2008) *Forensic science* 2nd edn. Harlow: Pearson Education p352
9	'Dennis Nilsen' *Wikipedia* https://www.en.wikipedia.org/wiki/Dennis_Nilsen
10	Schwark, T. et al. (2011) 'Reliable genetic identification of burnt human remains', *Forensic Science International*: Genetics 5, pp393-399
11	'John Haigh' *Wikipedia* https://www.en.wikipedia.org.wiki/John_Haigh
12	Simpson, K. (1980) *Forty years of murder.* St Albans: Granada Publishing pp197-199.
13	Topping, A. (2016) 'Man who dissolved PC Gordon Semple's body in acid jailed for life' *The Guardian* 12/12/16 [Online] https://www.the guardian.com/uk-news/2016/dec/12/police-officer-killer-jailed-for-life-stefano-brizzi-breaking-bad
14	*Vice* (2017) 'The life and crimes of 'cannibal cop killer' Stefano Brizzi' 21/02/17 [Online] https://www.vice.com/en_us/article/4xbxkq/the-life-and-crimes-of-cannibal-cop-killer-stefano-brizzi
15	Whyte, M. (2014) 'The acid test: Can you dissolve a body completely?' [Online] https://www.in-the-loop.net.au/acid-test-can-dissolve-body-completely/
16	Amadasi, A. et al. (2017) 'Assessment of the effects exerted by acid and alkaline solutions on bone: Is chemistry the answer?', *Journal of Forensic Sciences*, 62 pp1297-1303

17	*NBC news* (2007) 'Woman guilty of murdering husband with acid' 13/12/2007 [Online] http://www.nbcnews.com/id/22226173/ns/us_news-crime_and_courts/t/woman-guilty-murdering-husband-acid/#.W8TB1ntKjIU
18	*B.B.C.* (2009) 'Mexico man 'dissolved 300 bodies' 24/01/09 [Online] http://news.bbc.co.uk/1/hi/world/americas/7848611.stm
19	Burks, R. (2017) 'The acid (bath) test', *Chemistry World*, July 2017 p71.
20	Amadasi, A. *et al. op. cit*
21	ibid.
22	'Margaret Hogg' *Wikipedia* https://en.wikipedia.org/wiki/Margaret_Hogg
23	Brenzini, V. and Pathak, R. (2018). 'A comparison study of bloodstains on painted and cleaned surfaces with luminol', *Forensic Science International*, 289 pp79-82.
24	Bradley, D. (2017) 'Antimalarial boost helps reveal trace bloodstains', *Chemistry World*, [Online] https://www.chemistryworld.com/news/blood-will-out/3007543.article
25	Sultana, A. (n.d.) 'Chemical enhancement for the detection of bloodstains' [Online] www.academia.edu/1785361/Chemical_enhancement_for_detection_of_bloodstains
26	Farrar, A., Porter, G. and Renshaw, A. (2012) 'Detection of latent bloodstains beneath painted surfaces using reflected infrared photography', *Journal of Forensic Sciences*, 57 (5) pp1190-1198.
27	Brenzini, V. and Pathak, R. (2018) *op. cit.*
28	Murnaghan, I. (2016). 'Detecting evidence after bleaching', *Future of Forensics* 10/08/16 [Online] http://www.exploreforensics.co.uk/detecting-evidence-after-bleaching.html
29	'Becky Watts: How a hunt for a missing teen turned into a grim murder inquiry' *The Telegraph* 10/11/17 [Online] https://www.telegraph.co.uk/news/2017/11/10/becky-watts-murder-hunt-missing-teen-turned-grim-murder-inquiry/
30	Harris, K.A. et. al. (2006) 'The effect of cleaning agents on the DNA analysis of blood stains deposited on different substrates', *International Congress Series,* 1288 (2006) pp589-591

31	Passi, N. (2012) 'Effect of luminol and bleaching agent on the serological and DNA analysis from bloodstain', *Egyptian Journal of Forensic Sciences,* 2 pp54-61.
32	Bittencourt, E.A.A. et. al. (2009) 'The analysis of biological samples from crime scene for a future human DNA profile confrontation. Effects of presumptive test reagents on the ability to obtain STR profiles for human identification', *Forensic Science International: Genetics Supplement,* 2 (1) pp194-195

Further Information

There are no handy manuals on how to dispose of a body or clean up a crime scene although there are online fora where people pose such questions. The answers given should be viewed with some caution, however, and considered in the light of the material in this chapter. Real life cases are worth looking up, principally as a means of finding out what doesn't work. Dame Professor Sue Black's autobiographical book *All that remains* (Doubleday, 2018) contains some useful material on dismemberment.

Chapter 9

1	Bendelow, K. (2017) *The real CSI: a forensic handbook for crime writers.* Marlborough: Robert Hale p79.
2	Watson, N. in White, P.C. (ed.) (2016) *Crime scene to court: The essentials of forensic science* 4th edn. Cambridge: Royal Society of Chemistry p561
3	*Sense about Science* (2017) 'Making sense of forensic genetics' London: Sense about Science
4	McDermid, V. (2014) *Forensics: the anatomy of crime.* London: Profile Books pp150-151
5	Hopwood, A.J. et al. (2010) 'Integrated microfluidic system for rapid forensic DNA analysis: sample collection to DNA profile', *Analytical Chemistry,* 82 (16) pp6991-6999.
6	Thong, Z. (2015) 'Evaluation of the RapidHITTM 200 system: A comparative study of its performance with Maxwell® DNA IQTM/Identifier® Plus/ABI 3500xL workflow', *Forensic Science International: Genetics,* 19 pp22-27.
7	Watson, N. *op. cit.* pp556-557
8	Butler, J.M., Kline, M.C. and Coble, M.D. (2018) 'NIST interlaboratory studies involving DNA mixtures (MIX05 and MIX13): Variation observed and lessons learned', *Forensic Science International: Genetics,* 37 pp81-94.

9	Bittencourt, E.A.A. et. al. (2009) 'The analysis of biological samples from crime scene for a future human DNA profile confrontation. Effects of presumptive test reagents on the ability to obtain STR profiles for human identification', *Forensic Science International: Genetics Supplement*, 2 (1) pp194-195
10	Laville, S. (2018) 'DNA advances and officers' drive power cold-case successes' *The Guardian* 03/11/18
11	*Sense about Science* (2017) *op. cit.*
12	ibid.
13	Jackson, A.R.W., Jackson, J.M. and Mountain, H.M. (2008) *Forensic science* 2nd edn. Harlow: Pearson Education p164
14	Gallop, A. (2019) *When the dogs don't bark.* London: Hodder and Stoughton Chapter 20
15	Corbyn, Z. (2018) 'How home DNA tests are solving crimes' *The Observer* 02/12/18
16	Jackson, A.R.W., Jackson, J.M. and Mountain, H.M. (2008) *op. cit.* p180
17	Richmond, K. 2018 'Deconstructing DNA' *Law and science* [Online] https//lawandscienceweb.wordpress.com/2018/09/06/deconstructing-dna/
18	Morgan, R. (2018) Presentation at *Crime Science versus Crime Fiction* meeting, University College London, 30th August 2018. Available at https://mediacentral.ucl.ac.uk/Play/13700
19	Davis, N. (2017) 'DNA in the dock' *The Guardian* 02/10/17
20	ibid
21	Tully, G. 2018 *'Forensic science regulator: Overseeing quality'* Annual report November 2016-November 2017 Birmingham: The Forensic Science Regulator. www.gov.uk/government/organisations/forensic-science-regulator
22	*Mail Online* (2012) 'Teenager wrongly accused of rape because of DNA contamination is released from prison' 11/03/12 https://www.dailymail.co.uk/news/article-2113025/Teenager-wrongly-accused-rape-DNA-contamination-released-prison.html

Further information

There is much material available on DNA and the field is constantly changing so it is hard to keep up with developments unless you are working in the field. A particularly useful introduction to the subject is the Sense about Science publication *Making sense of forensic genetics.* The chapter in White's *From crime scene to court* is much more complicated and requires some biological knowledge to follow it.

Chapter 10

1	Bendelow, K. (2017) *The real CSI: A forensic handbook for crime writers.* Marlborough: Robert Hale p140.
2	Sansom, C. (2016) 'Separating the guilty and the innocent' *Chemistry World* November 2016 pp52-55
3	Heller, J.L. (2017). 'Toxicology screen' MedlinePlus 31/01/17. National Institutes of Health/U.S. National Library of Medicine [Online] https://medlineplus.gov/ency/article/003578.htm
4	*The Engineer* (2016) 'Saliva test for 'date rape' drug GHB' 08/01/16 [Online] https://www.theengineer.co.uk/saliva-test-for-date-rape-drug-ghb/
5	Drummer, O.H. (2006) 'Drug testing in oral fluid', *Clinical Biochemistry Reviews*, 27 (3) pp147-159
6	Cole, M. and Baron, M. in White, P.C. (ed.) (2016) *Crime scene to court: The essentials of forensic science* 4th edn. Cambridge: Royal Society of Chemistry Chapter 13
7	*B.B.C.* (2014) 'Brixton prison governor fails drug test after eating bread'.12/05/14 [Online] https://www.bbc.co.uk./news/england-london-27377788
8	Pélissier-Alicot, A-L. et. al. (2003) 'Mechanisms underlying postmortem redistribution of drugs: A review', *Journal of Analytical Toxicology,* 27 pp533-542
9	ibid
10	Verstraete, A.G. (2004) 'Detection times of drugs of abuse in blood, urine and oral fluid,' *Therapeutic Drug Monitoring,* 26 (2) pp200-204
11	Cox, T. (2017) 'Traces of sleeping drug found in Helen Bailey's hair, court told' *CambridgeshireLive*11/01/17 [Online] https://www.cambridge-news.co.uk/news/cambridge-news/traces-sleeping-drug-found-helen-12439381.
12	Berry, A and Wainwright, M, (2008) 'Shannon given sleeping drugs for nearly two years, kidnap trial told' *The Guardian* 20/11/08 [Online] https://www.theguardian.com/uk/2008/nov/20/shannon-drugs-court-trial
13	Mancuso, C.J and Ehleringer, J.R. (2019) 'Resident and non-resident fingernail isotopes reveal diet and travel patterns' *Journal of Forensic Sciences* 64 (1)

14	Department of Transport (2017) 'Changes to drug driving law' Updated 27/08/17 [Online] https://www.gov.uk/drug-driving-law
15	Extance, A. (2018) 'Spectroscopy in your hands', *Chemistry World*, February 2018 pp50-53
16	Chapman, K. (2018) 'A day at the body farm', *Chemistry World*, October 2018 pp56-57
17	Walsh, K.A.J and Horrocks, M. (2008) 'Palynology: Its position in the field of forensic science', *Journal of Forensic Sciences,* 53 (5) pp1053-1060.
18	Ireland, T. 2017. 'Code green', *The Biologist*, 64 (1) 22-25
19	Freshwater Habitats Trust (n.d.) 'What is eDNA?' [Online] https://freshwaterhabitats.org.uk/edna/edna
20	Cooper, R. 2012. 'Determining sex from a fingerprint', *Chemistry World,* 26/10/12 [Online] https://www.chemistryworld.com/news/determining-sex-from-a-fingerprint/5566.article
21	Hinners, P., O'Neill,K.C. and Lee, Y.J. (2018) 'Revealing individual lifestyles through mass spectrometry imaging of chemical compounds in fingerprints', *Nature Scientific Reports*, [Online] DOI:10.1038/s41598-018-23544-7
22	Bradshaw, R., Denison, N. and Francese, S. (2017) 'Implementation of MALDI MS profiling and imaging methods for the analysis of real crime scene fingermarks', Analyst, [Online] DOI:10.1039/c7an00218a
23	Russell, D. (2018) quoted in *Inside Science* B.B.C. Radio 4 01/11/18.
24	Guay, J. (2017) 'Forensics expert invents way to catch paedophiles with a photo of their hand' Apolitical Group Limited 06/10/17[Online] https://apolitical.co/solution_article/forensics-expert-invents-way-catch-paedophiles-photo-hand/
25	'Vein matching' *Wikipedia* https://en.wikipedia.org/wiki/Vein_matching
26	Pugh, R. (2019) 'Interview: Dame Sue Black' *The Guardian* 27/03/19
27	Kopfstein, J. (2016) 'I replaced my fingerprints with prosthetics to avoid surveillance' Motherboard 06/07/16 [Online] https://motherboard.vice.com/en_us/article/yp3nzb/i-replaced-my-fingerprints-with-prosthetics-to-avoid-surveillance

28	*Wikihow* (2018) 'How to fake fingerprints' Updated September 2018 [Online] https://wikihow.com/Fake-Fingerprints
29	Wogan, T. 2014 'Fingertip sweat pore maps to catch criminals,' *Chemistry World*, 14/05/14 [Online] https://www.chemistryworld.com/news/fingertip-sweat-pore-maps-to-catch-criminals/7361.article
30	Giles, A. in White, P.C. (ed.) (2016) *Crime scene to court: The essentials of forensic science* 4th edn. Cambridge: Royal Society of Chemistry pp229-259
31	ibid.
32	Burks, R. (2018) 'Pulp fiction?' *Chemistry World* May 2018 p71.
33	The Royal Society (2017) '*Forensic gait analysis: a primer for the courts*' London: The Royal Society
34	Gray, R. (2017) 'Gunfire audio opens new front in crime-fighting' *B.B.C.* 04/05/17 [Online] https://www.bbc.co.uk/news/science-environment-39621766
35	Case, A. (2018) 'On junk science, pop forensics and crime fiction' [Online] https://crimereads.com/on-junk-science-pop-forensics-and-crime-fiction/
36	Saks, M.J. (2010) 'Forensic identification: From a faith-based "science" to a scientific science', *Forensic Science International,* 201 pp14-17
37	Broeders, A.P.A. (2006) 'Of earprints, fingerprints, scent dogs, cot deaths and cognitive contamination - a brief look at the present state of play in the forensic arena', *Forensic Science International*, 159 pp148-57
38	McDermid, V. (2014) *Forensics: The anatomy of crime.* London: Profile Books pp130-133.
39	Morgan, R. (2018) 'The dangers of misinterpreted forensic evidence' TED Archive published 05/04/18 [Online] https://youtube.com/watch?v=xclg8ikPAv|
40	Trager, R. (2018a) 'Forensics in crisis,' *Chemistry World,* July 2018 pp21-27.
41	Crist, M. and Requarth, T. (2018) 'Forensic science put Jimmy Genrich in prison for 24 years. What if it wasn't science?' *The Nation* 26/02/18 [Online] https://www.thenation.com/article/the-crisis-of-american-forensics/
42	Morgan, R. (2018) *op. cit.*
43	Trager, R. (2018a) *op. cit*
44	Morgan, R. (2018) *op.cit.*

45	'Barry George' *Wikipedia* https://en.wikipedia.org/wiki/Barry_George
46	Associated Press (2014) 'Ex-CSI chief sentenced to prison for planting blood evidence in Neb. double-murder case' Fox News 20/11/14 [Online] https://foxnews.com/us/ec-csi-chief-sentenced-to-prison-for-planting-blood-evidence-in-neb-double-murder-case
47	Grimes, A.C. (2015) '10 heinous cases of misconduct by crime investigators' *Listverse* [Online] https://listverse.com/2015/02/06/10-heinous-cases-of-misconduct-by-crime-investigators/
48	Trager, R. (2018b) 'Thousands of US drug convictions overturned by rogue chemist's actions' *Chemistry World* January 2018 p10
49	*Chemistry World* (2017) '21,500 cases dismissed due to forensic chemist's misconduct' June 2017 p6
50	Trager, R. (2018a) *op. cit.*
51	Burke, M. (2018) 'Misconduct scandal hits UK forensics lab, *Chemistry World,* January 2018 p11'
52	Devlin, H. (2019) 'Forensic science labs "are on the brink of collapse"' *The Guardian* 01/05/19
53	Devlin, H. (2019) 'Forensics firm stripped of accreditation over handling of evidence from police' *The Guardian* 13/06/19

Further Information

Most of the topics discussed in this chapter are collected from a variety of journals, many of which can be found online without access to a university library.

For a basic introduction to forensics see Val McDermid's *Forensics* and Kate Bendelow's *The Real CSI* are well worth reading. *From Crime Scene to Court*, edited by White, and *Forensic Science*, by Jackson, Jackson and Mountain, are both textbooks requiring some scientific background. The work carried out at UCL's Jill Dando Institute of Security and Crime Science is particularly interesting - their website is at https://www.ucl.ac.uk/jill-dando-institute. For a picture of real life forensic science, including details of a number of famous cases, Angela Gallop's *When dogs don't bark* is excellent. I particularly recommend the blog *Locard's Lab* (https://locardslab.com) for updates on forensic techniques, interviews with practitioners and interesting cases. A useful Twitter contributor is @Scotland Yard CSI.

FICTION WORKS CITED IN THE TEXT

Chapt	Author	Year	Title	Publisher
1	Bolton, S.J.	2009	*Awakening*	Bantam
	Christie, A.	1936	*Cards on the Table*	Collins
	Christie, A.	1939	*Murder is Easy*	Collins
	Christie, A.	1945	*Sparkling Cyanide*	Collins
	Christie, A.	1961	*The Pale Horse*	Collins
	Finch, P.	2015	*Hunted*	Avon
	Fleming, I.	1958	*Dr. No*	Jonathan Cape
	Fowler, C.	2010	*Bryant and May Off the Rails*	Doubleday
	James, P.	2016	*Love You Dead*	Macmillan
	Reichs, K.	2011	*Flash and Bones*	William Heinemann
	Sayers, D.L.	1930	*Strong Poison*	Gollancz
2	Abbott, R.	2014	*Sleep Tight*	Black Dot
	Child, L.	2017	*Midnight Line*	Bantam
	Christie, A.	1921	*The Mysterious Affair at Styles*	The Bodley Head
	Christie, A.	1927	*The Big Four*	Collins
	Christie, A.	1929	*The House of Lurk-ing Death* in *Partners in Crime*	Collins
	Christie, A.	1935	*Three Act Tragedy*	Collins
	Christie, A.	1938	*Appointment with Death*	Collins
	Christie, A.	1939	*Murder is Easy*	Collins
	Christie, A.	1940	*Sad Cypress*	Collins
	Christie, A.	1942	*Five Little Pigs*	Collins
	Christie, A.	1957	*The 4:50 from Paddington*	Collins
	Christie, A.	1968	*By the Pricking of my Thumbs*	Collins
	Doyle, A.C.	1890	*The Sign of Four*	Lippincott's Monthly Magazine
	Fleming, I.	1957	*From Russia with Love*	Jonathan Cape

Chapt	Author	Year	Title	Publisher
	Fleming, I.	1958	*Dr. No*	Jonathan Cape
	MacBride, S.	2017	*A Dark so Deadly*	Harper Collins
	Moore, J.	2016	*The Poison Artist*	Orion
	Owen, W.	c1917	*Dulce et decorum est* Anthologised in *Out in the dark: Poetry of the First World War*	Saxon Books
	Rendell, R	1979	*Means of Evil* in *Means of Evil and Other Stories*	Hutchinson
	Rendell, R.	1982	*Thornapple* in *The Fever Tree*	Hutchinson
	Rendell, R.	1995	*Shreds and Slivers* in *Blood Lines*	Hutchinson
	Rendell, R.	1995	Unacceptable Levels in *Blood Lines*	Hutchinson
3	Arlidge, M.J.	2018	*Down to the Woods*	Michael Joseph
	Bolton, S	2016	*Daisy in Chains*	Corgi
	Carver, C.J.	2016	*Spare Me the Truth*	Zaffre
	James, P.	2015	*You are Dead*	Macmillan
	James, P.D.	1962	*Cover Her Face*	Faber and Faber
	Reichs, K.	2016	*The Bone Collection*	Heinemann
	Robotham, M.	2015	*Close Your Eyes*	Sphere
	Simms, C.	2017	*High Flyer* in Edwards, M. (ed.) *Mystery tour: A Crime Writers Association anthology*	Orenda Books
4	James, P.	2016	*Love you Dead*	Macmillan
	Pullman, P.	1995	*Northern Lights*	Scholastic
5	Bale, T.	2017	*Each Little Lie*	Bookouture
	Dickens, C.	1853	*Bleak House*	Bradbury and Evans

Chapt	Author	Year	Title	Publisher
	O'Donnell, P.	1976	*Last day in Limbo*	Souvenir Press
	Post, M.D.	1914	*The Doomdorf Mystery* in Penzler, O. (ed.) (2014) *The Locked Room Mysteries*	Corvus
6	Armstrong, R.	2018	*Head Case*	HQ
	Atkinson, K.	2007	*One Good Turn*	Black Swan
	Child, L.	2005	*One Shot*	Bantam
	Child, L.	2015	*Personal*	Bantam
	Doyle, A.C.	1905	*The Empty House* in *The Return of Sherlock Holmes*	George Newnes
	Finch, P.	2014	*The Killing Club*	Avon
	Grey, I.	2016	*Shot Through the Heart*	Quercus
	Hill, R.	1970	*A Clubbable Woman*	Collins
	Sharp, Z.	2018	*Dancing on the Grave*	ZACE
7	Arlidge, M.J.	2018	*Down to the Woods*	M. Joseph
	Galbraith, R.	2018	*Lethal White*	Sphere
	McCormick, W.B.	2017	*Matricide and Ice Cream* in Edwards, M. (ed.) *Mystery tour: A Crime Writers Association* anthology	Orenda Books
	McDermid, V.	2015	*Splinter the Silence*	Little, Brown
	Steiner, S.	2018	*Persons Unknown*	The Borough Press
8	Cavanagh, S.	2018	*Th1rt3en*	Orion
	Craven, M.W.	2018	*The Puppet Show*	Constable
	Fowler, C.	2018	*Hall of Mirrors*	Doubleday
10	Freeman,	1907	*The Red Thumb Mark*	Resurrected Press (reprint 2010)
	Sayers, D.L. (	1930	*Strong Poison*	Gollancz

FILM AND TELEVISION REFERENCES

Chapter 1

a. *Foyle's War* (2002-2015). A B.B.C. detective series created by Anthony Horowitz set during, and shortly after, WWII.
b. *The Bridge* season 4 (2018) A Danish/Swedish detective series created by Hans Rosenfeldt, broadcast by the B.B.C. in the U.K.

Chapter 2

a. *Midsomer Murders* (1997 -) A rural detective series originally based on books by Caroline Graham, broadcast on ITV in the U.K.
b. *House of Cards* (2013-2018) A U.S. political thriller created by Beau Willimon, based on a B.B.C. series created by Michael Dobbs, starring Kevin Spacey and Robin Wright and broadcast on Netflix.
c. *Taggart* (1983-2010) A Scottish detective series created by Glenn Chandler, broadcast on ITV in the U.K.

Chapter 3

a. *The Man From U.N.C.L.E.* (1964-1968) A U.S. TV spy series created by Sam Rolfe, broadcast on NBC in the U.S. and the B.B.C. in the U.K.

Chapter 4

a. *Shameless* (2004-2018) A British black comedy series, created by Paul Abbott, set on a fictional council estate in Manchester, broadcast on Channel 4 in the U.K. A U.S. version was also produced.
b. *Cracker* (1993-2006) A British crime series, created by Jimmy McGovern, featuring a forensic psychologist. A U.S. version was also produced.
c. *Bodyguard* (2018) A B.B.C. drama, written by Jed Mercurio, featuring a politician's bodyguard.

Chapter 5

a. *New Tricks* (2003-2015) A B.B.C. crime series featuring retired police detectives recruited to form a cold case squad.
b. *New Tricks* (as above)

Chapter 6

a. *Dirty Harry* (1971) A U.S. crime thriller directed by Don Siegel, starring Clint Eastwood as a maverick San Francisco police officer.
b. *Terminator 2: Judgement Day* (1991) A science fiction thriller directed by James Cameron, starring Arnold Schwarzenegger and Linda Hamilton.
c. *Lock, Stock and Two Smoking Barrels* (1998) A London-set crime comedy-thriller written and directed by Guy Ritchie.

Chapter 7

a. *Goldfinger* (1964) A British spy thriller directed by Guy Hamilton, starring Sean Connery as James Bond.
b. *The Net* (1995) A U.S. cyber thriller directed by Irwin Winkler starring Sandra Bullock as a computer expert.
c. *Black Widow* (1987) A U.S. thriller starring Theresa Russell as a serial husband-killer.
d. *Midsomer Murders* (1997 -) A rural detective series originally based on books by Caroline Graham, broadcast on ITV in the U.K.

Chapter 8

a. *New Tricks* (2003-2015) A B.B.C. crime series featuring retired police detectives recruited to form a cold case squad.
b. *Foyle's War* (2002-2015). A B.B.C. detective series created by Anthony Horowitz set during, and shortly after, WWII.
c. *Breaking Bad* (2008-2013) A U.S. crime drama created by Vince Gilligan, starring Bryan Cranston and Aaron Paul, which was broadcast on AMC in the US and Netflix elsewhere.
d. *Taggart* (1983-2010) A Scottish detective series created by Glenn Chandler, broadcast on ITV in the U.K.
e. *Goldfinger* (1964) A British spy thriller directed by Guy Hamilton, starring Sean Connery as James Bond.
f. *Fargo* (1996) A U.S. black comedy/crime drama directed by Joel and Ethan Coen, starring Frances McDormand as a pregnant police officer.
g. *Snatch* (2000) A British crime comedy film written and directed by Guy Ritchie.
h. *Taggart* (see above)

Chapter 10

a. & b *CSI: Crime Scene Investigation* (2000-2015) The first of a series of CBS forensic crime dramas, created by Anthony E. Zuiker, set in several U.S. cities
c. *Crimewatch (*1984-2017) A B.B.C. TV series which used professional presenters, police officers and reconstructions to appeal to the public for help in solving crimes.

GLOSSARY

Adipocere	The waxy material coating a body after prolonged immersion in water.
Alkali	The opposite of an acid, strong examples of which can be highly corrosive e.g. caustic soda (sodium hydroxide).
Alkaloids	A group of nitrogen-containing substances found in plants, many of which have been used as drugs or poisons.
Amelogenin	A genetic marker used to identify the sex of a person leaving a DNA sample.
Antihistamine	One of a group of drugs used as mild sedatives, to reduce skin irritation and to prevent travel sickness.
Autoignition temperature	The temperature at which a mixture of flammable gas or vapour, with air, will automatically ignite.
Cardiac tamponade	The buildup of blood in the chest cavity which prevents the heart from beating.
Char	The material (mainly carbon) left after wood or other organic material has been heated and the volatile substances driven off.
Charge	An assemblage of explosive material intended to do a particular job e.g. demolition.
Chain reaction	A chemical or physical process, where the products of the process keep the process going, for instance combustion where the products initiate further combustion.
Combustion products	Substances, usually gases and liquids, produced as material burns.
Compound chemical	A substance of fixed composition, usually consisting of two or more elements, not easily separable into its components by physical means (contrasts with a mixture).
Controlled drug	A drug subject to the U.K. Misuse of Drugs Act 1971 and subsequent legislation, possession and supply of which without appropriate authority is an offence.
COPD	**Chronic obstructive pulmonary disease:** A progressive disease which makes breathing increasingly difficult.
CS	An incapacitating spray used by police forces.
Dactyloscopy	Fingerprint analysis.
Deflagrate	To flare up when ignited.

Electrophoresis	A process used in DNA profiling which separates fragments using an electric field.
Element	One of 92 natural,or artificial, substances which cannot be broken down into simpler chemicals, forming the building blocks for all chemicals.
Enzyme	A protein used as a catalyst to regulate processes in the body from growth and development to the metabolism of food and other substances.
Epicentre	The point on the earth's surface directly above the origin of an earthquake (not the middle of a riot, explosion or other disturbance).
Flashpoint	The temperature at which a liquid gives off enough vapour to form a flammable mixture with air, under prescribed test conditions.
Free radicals	Chemicals which react aggressively with other substances - produced in fires (among other processes) and important for sustaining combustion.
FSB	The Russian Federal Security Service, formerly KGB
Gastrointestinal tract	The tube running from the mouth to the anus.
Genome	The sum total of genes in an organism.
Haemoglobin	The red pigment in blood cells which picks up oxygen in the lungs and conveys it to the rest of the body.
Hyperglycaemia	Too much glucose in the blood.
Hypoglycaemia	Too little glucose in the blood
Incendiary	A device intended to set fire to things
Inert gases	A group of gases including helium, argon and neon which very rarely combine with other substances
Inorganic	Substances generally based on elements other than carbon
Ion	An electrically charged particle in solution or in a high-temperature cloud of gas
LD50	The dose of a poison which kills 50% of a test population of animals
Locus	A defined section of the DNA molecule, plural loci
Low copy number	Refers to a sample where there are very small amounts of DNA present
Metabolite	The result of biochemical processes within the body acting on an absorbed substance,
Microgram	One millionth of a gram
Milligram	One thousandth of a gram

Molecule	The smallest possible particle of a chemical compound
Mucous membranes	Moist membranes lining body cavities such as the mouth and vagina
Nanogram	One thousand-millionth of a gram
Nucleus	The central part of a cell or an atom
Organic	Substances based on carbon which were originally thought could only be made by living processes. In agriculture, without the use of synthetic fertilisers or pesticides.
Organophosphorus	Refers to a group of organic chemicals, often toxic, which contain the element phosphorus
Oxidation	The process by which substances combine with oxygen, usually involving the release of heat
Oxidising agent	An oxygen-rich substance which facilitates combustion, e.g ammonium nitrate, hydrogen peroxide
Palynology	The study of pollen
PAVA	A police pepper-like spray used to incapacitate
Peptides	Small to medium-sized molecules consisting of amino-acids strung together
Phenotype	The characteristics of an organism resulting from the expression of its genes
Pneumothorax	Air in the chest cavity preventing the lungs working
Polymerase Chain Reaction (PCR)	A technique used to multiply traces of DNA in a sample so that it can be analysed
Porton Down	The U.K.'s chemical and biological defence research station on Salisbury Plain
Propellant	The material in a cartridge/rocket which burns quickly but smoothly, releasing propelling gases.
Pyrolysis	The heating of an organic material, e.g. wood, producing flammable gases and liquids
Pyrophoric	Catching fire spontaneously in air
Radioactivity	The property of an element which causes it to emit radiation
Radiation	Particles or rays emitted by a range of processes, including radioactivity.
STR	Short Tandem Repeats - sections of DNA used for identification purposes
Subcutaneous	Below the skin, referring either to a layer of fat or an injection
Taphonomy	The study of what happens to a body after death
THC	Tetrahydrocannabinol - found in cannabis
Vapour	Gas emitted from a liquid as it evaporates

Index

A

B

D

E

F

G

H

I

J

K

L

M

N

Q

R

S

T

U

V

W

Y

Z